ON HIS FIRST LEAVE

by

Sue Hatt

On His First Leave

Sue Hatt

ISBN: 978-1-9163163-0-0

Published by Sue Hatt Publishing in conjunction with Writersworld. This book is produced entirely in the UK, is available to order from most book shops in the United Kingdom, and is globally available via UK-based Internet book retailers and www.amazon.com.

Copy edited by Ian Large

Cover design by Jag Lall

Background image: Free Stock Textures

www.writersworld.co.uk

WRITERSWORLD
2 Bear Close Flats
Bear Close
Woodstock
Oxfordshire
OX20 1JX
United Kingdom

☎ 01993 812500

☎ +44 1993 812500

The text pages of this book are produced via an independent certification process that ensures the trees from which the paper is produced come from well managed sources that exclude the risk of using illegally logged timber while leaving options to use post-consumer recycled paper as well.

For my grandchildren,
Daniel, Alex, JoJo, James and Robin

Pat

Many thanks for support at Book Club.

Best wishes

Sue

ACKNOWLEDGEMENTS

This book would never have been written without the help of family and friends, old and new. My husband, John, has been a constant source of support and encouragement and has listened tirelessly as I have talked him through all the trials and tribulations of the writing process. My sister, Prue, and my daughter, Amy, read my early drafts and gave me valuable feedback, helping me develop our family story, and Pam Evans provided feedback from outside the family circle.

Writing *On His First Leave* has brought me into contact with many interesting people whom I am now pleased to count as friends. I am particularly grateful to Ingram Murray and his wife Juliet, who generously showed me around Hazebrouck, Joli-Bois and Wahagnies and to the Soldiers of Oxfordshire Museum which helped me to research the gaps in my story and provided useful detail about the Buckinghamshire Battalion.

I have tried to keep my account true to the record of the 1st Bucks Battalion's history in the early months of the Second World War but any mistakes are entirely my own. Writing a novel about actual events brings its own difficulties and some names have been fictionalised to preserve anonymity.

In the latter stages of the book's development I

have been lucky enough to have ongoing support from the Caldicot Writers Group who have patiently listened to my weekly 'episodes' and provided constructive feedback. Finally, my friends from the Curtis Brown Creative Course have helped me sort out the last few glitches, in particular Jen Weller, Zenia Dimitrakopoulou and Gautam Das.

Thanks to all of you.

PROLOGUE

England, May 2013

"Throw that away," said the voice from the chair. "Nobody wants that old thing."

"What is it, Mum?" I held up a cardboard shoe box, tied with bias binding, dusky pink and fraying at the edges. She had asked me to help sort through the clutter in a battered old suitcase, her treasures she called them, the things she had saved from her long life. Out came a dusty copy of the Coronation Supplement of *The Times* from 1953, an invitation to dinner with the Queen at Windsor Castle, some black and white photographs of her aunts, stiff and unsmiling, and then this old shoe box.

"It's my love letters."

"May I look?" I turned the box over in my hands, intrigued as I realised that the bias binding stood for the red ribbon that girls tied around their keepsakes. She nodded and her thick white hair shone in the sunlight as my fingers twitched at the tape. I untied the knot and took off the lid. Letters and postcards struggled to burst out, each one addressed to the girl she used to be.

I selected one letter near the beginning and one at the end. The first was postmarked January 1940 and contained several pages of thick notepaper, with a battalion emblem embossed at the top; it felt confident with strong pen strokes asserting the author's authority. At the end of the box lay a thin, airmail form, torn and stained, the pencilled writing fading as if his assurance were eroded. I had before me letters spanning the most momentous years of the twentieth century, the Second World War.

I looked around the room where my parents had spent their final years together. Family photos stood on the windowsill, the Staffordshire china adorned the shelves and the homemade curtains framed the windows. I had seen these things, sensed this homely atmosphere in all their houses. Through the patio doors I could hear the blackbird, Dad's blackbird she called it, its liquid notes drifting into the room. I knew it couldn't be Dad's blackbird, the one that had sung when he was dying; he had been gone too long for that. But Dad's blackbird, Dad's letters, I thought, an echo of his voice.

"No-one's interested in those old things. Time to throw them away." She found it tiring thinking back to days long forgotten when she was young and in love.

"Look, Mum, you mustn't throw these letters away." I felt a sense of urgency; this seemed important. "The Imperial War Museum would want them and anyway, I'm interested."

"Well, you take them then and do something with them," she said. So, that was it; I had her consent – and a commission too.

As I read the letters, I felt as if I was looking in one of those funny mirrors, the ones that make your legs too long, your head too wide; the staid grown-ups from my childhood re-emerged as different people. I could recognise their images, but they were strangely distorted.

The story began in the summer of 1939, before the war shattered their settled lives…

CHAPTER 1

England, July 1939

"Can I help you Mum?" said Margery as she and Brian came into the kitchen hand-in-hand. Brian squinted in the dim light. An old pear tree grew close to the window, casting the room into a perpetual shade. He saw the laden tea tray standing on the table and the teapot warming on the stove while the kettle came to the boil. The wooden tea caddy sat beside the clock on a shelf above the stove.

"No, thanks, it's nearly ready," said Nellie taking a batch of scones from the oven and putting them on the table before she turned to face the young couple. Nellie was a large woman and her children, Margery and Johnnie, took after her. Nellie always made Brian feel welcome; he had been a regular visitor, first as Johnnie's friend and then as Margery's suitor.

"You two go along and see Johnnie and Norah while I make the tea," said Nellie, picking up the tea towel to lift the kettle from the stove.

Brian ran his fingers through his fair curls and squeezed Margery's hand. Together they crossed the kitchen, tiptoed over the narrow hallway that ran the length of the bungalow and opened the living room door. The air smelled musty and damp; the bones of the old cottage never dried out, not even in summer. Brian winked at Margery as they entered the sitting room. Beside the door the table was laid for tea while, at the far end of the room, the sun sparkled on the decorative horse brasses hanging by the empty fireplace. The sofa squeaked as Johnnie and Norah rearranged themselves like guilty children.

"Norah, how nice to see you." Margery crossed the room, ignored her brother and kissed her friend. "I do hope Johnnie wasn't being too tedious."

Norah pulled her tweed skirt straight and returned the kiss. She was dark haired and small-boned – refined her mother said.

"Good to see you, old boy," said Johnnie, rising to shake hands with his old school friend. Johnnie was several inches taller than Brian, had thick dark hair and a moustache, the mark of an Army officer. "I'll bet you two enjoyed your ride. Glorious day for it. Did you have a gallop up Cuckoo Hill?"

"Margery did," said Brian. He looked at his feet and picked an invisible fleck off his sports jacket.

"Oh? And what about you?" Johnnie raised his eyebrows. He and Margery were natural riders at ease on a horse, at one with the motion. Brian was new to horsemanship and felt awkward in the saddle. He had learned to ride in the Territorial Army at the insistence of his colonel.

"I took a bit of a tumble, but no harm done; I fell in the heather."

"Hard luck, old boy. It's a good job we won't have to mount a cavalry charge against Herr Hitler, eh?"

"I'm not sure old B-B, my colonel, knows that; he's a bit behind the times," Brian said and they were all laughing as Nellie walked in with the tea tray, loaded with scones, jam, cream, sponge cake, fruit cake and chocolate finger biscuits. Brian loved Nellie's teas; his mother believed in plain wholesome food in modest portions, thin slices of brown bread and one piece of shortbread. They sat round the oak table and he took a scone still warm from the oven, the butter melting into its crumbling folds.

"How's your mother keeping?" Nellie asked Brian for news of her erstwhile neighbour.

"She's well enough, thank you, but she finds the grandchildren tiring."

"She is lucky to have them. I'd be glad of some." Nellie looked at Margery and Johnnie. Then she turned her attention to the rest of Brian's siblings; he came from a large family. As she began to ask about mutual acquaintances, Johnnie's patience wore thin.

"Really Mum, what a grilling for poor old Bri. You sound like the Chief Inquisitor. 'And where were you, Sir, on the evening of the 19th?'" Johnnie pulled a solemn face as he took an imaginary notebook from his top pocket.

"That's enough of that, cheeky boy!" Nellie said. Brian enjoyed the playful exchange; his family had to conduct themselves with decorum at the tea table. He offered cigarettes to Johnnie and Nellie – Churchman's, that was his brand.

"What was that Red Cross course like, Curly?" Johnnie called Margery by the nickname that played on her stubbornly straight hair. "Gas wasn't it?"

"That's right. I learned a lot. Gas can do such wretched things; I hate to think of you boys facing it." Margery had already enrolled in the Red Cross Voluntary Aid Detachment as a nursing auxiliary, a VAD. If war was declared she would work in a local hospital while Brian and Johnnie would serve in the Territorial Army, the part-time reservists.

"Will there really be a war, do you think?" said Margery. "All these parties are such fun this summer. I don't want anything to spoil it."

"My dad's jolly worried," said Norah.

"Aren't we all?" said Johnnie, raising his eyebrows and looking at Brian.

"All my brothers went to France last time," said Nellie. "I don't want Johnnie going off like that."

"Don't get in a state, Mum," said Johnnie.

Brian couldn't remember the Great War; that was just old people's talk. He stubbed out his cigarette and met Johnnie's gaze. They both knew that the country teetered on the edge of another war – their war, for their generation. Brian found the prospect both exciting and horrifying. War would open opportunities; he had never been overseas and he longed to travel, meet new people, stretch his horizons; but, at the same time, he recoiled from those grim horrors like gas.

"Chamberlain promised us 'Peace in our Time'. He said he'd done a deal with Hitler," said Nellie.

"I'm not sure Hitler can be trusted to keep his word." Johnnie blew out a stream of smoke.

"Nor am I," said Brian, stubbing out his cigarette.

"We can't let him walk all over Europe, can we Bri?"

"No indeed. At least Chamberlain's given us time to get ready. We've doubled the size of our battalion since Munich."

"We'll have to put a stop to it if he dares to go into Poland. And after all, Curly's just longing to dress up in her nurse's uniform."

"What will you do, Norah, if it comes?" Margery asked.

"I'd like to drive an ambulance but it depends on my mother." Everyone went quiet. Brian knew that, in Norah's family, her mother's word was law.

"When are you off to camp, Brian?" said Johnnie.

"Next week. Two weeks by the sea in Sussex."

"Oh, what a shame! You'll miss the tennis party at the Vicarage," said Norah. Brian knew these tennis parties well; they were a ritual – plenty of gossip, a bit of tennis, and pippy raspberry jam for tea.

"All the usual crowd are going – Margery, Johnnie, Mary and Donald, of course. He's got such a good serve," Norah said. Brian felt as if a cloud had hidden the sun. He knew that Donald, so serious, so full of big ideas, was sweet on Margery, his rival for her hand.

"So… Donald's down from Oxford, is he? What's he going to do now?"

"He could go into the nursery and grow rhododendrons with his father," said Margery. "But, given the situation, he's thinking of joining the RAF. One of his chums has an uncle who's a Wing Commander and can wangle a place for him."

"Posh lot the RAF," said Brian. "Not like us foot sloggers in the Light Infantry." He tried not to think of her playing tennis with Donald. Brian had never been happier than this summer… with Margery. He had partnered her at tennis, at dances, at bridge and he knew he had fallen in love. Perhaps he had always been in her thrall, even in the days of children's parties; she was the star in his heaven, the sun in his sky; but… he had to go away, to camp and then… who knows? Perhaps he needed to speak sooner rather than later. With the situation in Europe, he felt a sense of urgency, as if he were running for a bus, heart beating, lungs gasping, as he tried to clutch the handrail before it moved off.

After tea, Brian and Margery made their way down the garden to check on the horses. The stables greeted them with that peculiarly sweet mixture of sweat, straw and manure.

"Do you remember what fun we had getting in the hay?" Margery asked.

Brian nodded, his eyes never leaving her face. Those long evenings in the hay field were etched in his memory; they had both been so happy, so carefree. Margery had leaned against the haystack, a smudge on her cheek, her green eyes shining and he had pressed against her, the wisps of hay tickling his face as he caressed her, kissed her, and ached for her.

Jack, the hunter, quietly munched his hay and, in the neighbouring stall, stood Joey, the little black pony; he came over, looking for an apple. Margery gave him one and he crunched it noisily, spreading the juice over her hand. In the dying light, Brian took Margery in his arms and kissed her. He felt the soft warmth of her body as his moustache brushed against her cheek. He found her lips and, as she melted against him, he knew he could delay no longer.

"Margery, will you marry me?"

Margery pulled back and looked down.

"Oh, Brian, please don't spoil it. We're such good chums and we're having loads of fun. I don't want to marry anyone yet."

Brian felt as if he had been punched in the stomach, all his hopes, all his dreams shattered. He wanted more, so much more, than friendship.

CHAPTER 2

England, September 1939

"What time is he going to speak?" asked Margery, turning from the sink as Johnnie came into the kitchen. She was helping Nellie with the Sunday lunch.

"11.15, just after the deadline expires."

Nellie took the meat out of the oven, its rich aroma filling the air; she basted it and returned the roasting tray to the stove where it sizzled and spat. Outside the open door a blackbird sang but they had ears for nothing but the radio. As the Prime Minister's voice crackled over the airwaves, they sat at the kitchen table and listened.

"This morning the British Ambassador in Berlin handed the German Government a final note stating that, unless we heard from them by 11 o'clock that they were prepared to withdraw their troops from Poland, a state of war would exist between us.

"I have to tell you now that no such undertaking has been received, and that consequently this country is at war with Germany."

When he finished, they remained silent, each one locked in a private world assessing the implications, the personal repercussions, of that declaration.

"That's it then," said Johnnie, the first to speak as usual. "No more shilly-shallying. Hitler's got it coming to him; we'll soon put a stop to his antics."

Margery knew he was putting a brave face on it. She had heard about his Army training, drilling with broomsticks instead of guns, ammunition shortages and not enough boots to go around. The country seemed as ill-prepared for war as she felt herself to be. She took the roasting tin out of the oven and added the potatoes as their neighbour, Fleda, burst through the door, her ebullient personality crowding the room. She put her hymn book and gloves on the table between the batter for the Yorkshire pudding and the runner beans. She wore a plain grey suit and flat brown shoes. She reached up to remove her felt hat and her wiry curls sprung around her face.

"Mmm, something smells good." Fleda settled herself at the table and took out her cigarettes. "I suppose you've heard the news. The vicar announced in church that we are at war."

"We listened to Chamberlain," said Johnnie. "It's a grim business."

"It's a confounded nuisance, I say. Even though I was only a child, I can remember the Great War. We couldn't get anyone to help in the house or the garden as everyone was on war service."

"I shouldn't think that'll worry you much," said Margery. "Your house is full of cobwebs and the garden is so overgrown that your cottage seems like a goldfish bowl." Despite the news, they all laughed as Johnnie handed round the sherry.

"I suppose you'll have to go, Johnnie," said Fleda. Nellie clung to Johnnie, always her favourite, her feelings heightened by his imminent danger.

"Yes, the only question is when. I saw Brian in Windsor yesterday; the Bucks are expecting to be called up immediately. They'll be gone to France by Christmas, I shouldn't wonder."

Margery looked away, her face glum. Brian had not been to Stone Cottage since the day of their ride, the day of his question, and she found she missed him. She had enjoyed his company, had liked being a foursome with Johnnie and Norah, had appreciated his quiet concern for her comfort. He was a good sort and she had wanted their easy relationship to go on, unchanged, like a comfortable old frock. But, as the long summer days drew in, she began to realise that their lives were about to change forever.

"I'll have to close my business." Fleda had been pioneering new strains of high yielding hens. "Everything will be geared to the war effort now."

"Gosh," said Margery. "Will you mind?"

"Not really. I'm ready for a change. Who knows? I might come nursing with you; mopping fevered brows and helping surgeons, it all sounds rather fun." Fleda took a sip of her sherry and turned to Nellie. "You might want to have a few of my hens."

"Why would I want hens? Dirty old things, scratching everything up."

"Actually Mum, I think it's a jolly good idea," said Johnnie. "Food's going to be scarce and a ready supply of eggs could be useful."

"Mmm, I'll think about it," said Nellie and Margery knew she would be won over by her son.

"You look very professional," said Nellie as Margery walked into the kitchen wearing her VAD uniform, a plain blue dress, an apron with a red cross on the bib and her nurse's cap.

"I don't feel it," Margery said. She sat at the table and reached down to stroke Judy's head as the spaniel thumped her tail on the floor. "I'm so tall that I stick out like a sore thumb. What if I do something dreadful?"

"I'm sure you won't. A good breakfast and a cup of tea will soon settle you down." Food and tea were Nellie's cure-all.

"I don't think I could eat a mouthful, Mum."

"Nonsense. Of course, you can. You're not going without your breakfast; you can't do a full day's work on an empty stomach and I've saved two eggs especially for you. I'm awfully glad that I took those hens of Fleda's. They're still laying, you know, and that's useful now everything is getting scarce." Knowing she couldn't resist, Margery sat down at the table to eat her eggs.

The bike ride to Brookwood Hospital steadied her nerves. She pedalled along in the crisp autumn morning with the leaves changing colour, the berries red on the hawthorn hedges and the spiders' webs glistening with dew. Margery arrived in good time – it would be dreadful to be late on the first day – and she gathered with the other trainees in the entrance hall. Their Red Cross officer took them to their wards and they marched through the hospital grounds, feeling like new girls on their first day at school.

"Nurse Street, Nurse Blackwell, this is your ward. Off you go and report to Sister." The two girls looked at each other as they scurried through the swing doors; their feet clicked on the lino as they walked between the iron bedsteads towards Sister's desk.

"We've got some new patients coming in this morning. I want you to make up the beds. I suppose you know how to do that?" Sister looked askance at the newcomers standing before her, their hands behind their backs; Margery guessed that she doubted the value of VADs on her ward.

"Yes, Sister." Their voices sounded more confident than they felt; hospital corners could be so tricky.

"Off you go then."

The ward rang with noise, shoes echoing on the lino, the tea trolley clattering, and the doors banging. A distinctive smell pervaded the atmosphere, a mix of disinfectant, stale cabbage and freshly laundered sheets. The London doctors in their white coats were at ease in the hospital environment and the nurses seemed so sure of themselves, so professional; they had been evacuated from St Thomas's Hospital in London, and their competence overwhelmed Margery, the wartime volunteer, and a local one at that.

"Nurse Street, I want you to give Mrs Collins a blanket bath," said Sister, appearing at Margery's side as if from nowhere.

"Yes, Sister," Margery said. She had been trained for this, but would she remember it all?

"Hello, Mrs Collins. I'm Nurse Street and I'm going to get you ready for your operation. I'll fetch the screens and then we'll get you all clean for the doctor. Where is it you live?"

"In Knaphill, Nurse. Just down Anchor Hill, in one of those cottages near the pub. We don't have a bathroom, you know. Just a tap in the kitchen."

"I know those cottages," said Margery, starting her work. "They've got such lovely gardens. I've often been down that way to play tennis with my friends."

"You're a local girl, are you?"

"Yes, indeed. I live in West End with my mother. My brother's in the Army now."

"Our boy's gone too, for training they say."

Chatting away, Margery got the work done. She scrubbed floors, made beds and polished lockers until lunch time. During the afternoon one of the doctors approached and Margery noticed his good looks, his fair hair and blue eyes; he spoke with a slight accent, an Australian perhaps.

"Could you find me some screens Nurse? I want to examine, Mrs Black."

"Of course, Doctor."

"You're new, aren't you?" he said when he'd finished, his eyes crinkling as he smiled at her.

"Yes, it's my first day."

"You'll soon get the hang of it. We've none of us been here long. It feels a bit strange for me; I only started at St Thomas's in June. It's a rabbit warren, that place, and I had just begun to find my way around when we moved down here."

"Where do you come from?"

"Oh, the accent you mean. I'm from Cape Town, South Africa."

Wow, thought Margery. How exotic! She had never been out of England.

"Gosh, that's quite a way to come."

"My dad trained at St Thomas's and he wanted the same for me but now he's not so sure, with the bombs and all that." He turned to write up the notes. I'm going to enjoy working here, Margery thought.

Brian felt confused. The light seemed to be coming from the wrong side, that weak September light, reluctant to admit that summer had gone. Where could he be? Certainly not in his own bedroom at Ditham Croft, his parents' house. The sounds were wrong too; the thump of heavy boots, loud voices and the clatter of pans. As he shook away the remnants of sleep, he remembered: he was with the battalion, training at Newbury racecourse, cooped up in the Jockeys' Hospital with the other officers. Wartime now and he'd got a job to do, a job that kept him busy and pushed away the heartbreak. He got out of his narrow bed and completed his morning routine – washing, shaving, dressing.

"Are you ready, Brian? Shall we go to breakfast together?" said Simon. He and Brian had been in the battalion in peacetime; they had trained at weekends, drilled in Slough and attended summer camps. Simon was clean shaven and his face exuded good humour and confidence. He and Brian had shared many a joke together and they sat side by side on a bench in the Mess with their plates of bacon and eggs, fried bread and fried tomatoes. A wooden board on the wall proclaimed the winners of the Newbury Cup and there were several pictures of racehorses around the room. The smell of fat filled the air.

"What have you got on this morning, old boy?" Simon asked, wiping his plate with a slice of toast.

"Confounded paperwork," said Brian, stabbing at his bacon. "It's a nightmare for a company commander. Forms for boots, forms for uniforms, forms for equipment, forms for pay. I suppose I'll get the hang of it but it's enough to drive me bonkers."

"Would you rather be back in the bank then?"

"No fear." Brian sipped his tea. He had wanted to go into the police force but he was too short. The bank had been his father's idea, a job with good prospects, he said, but Brian found it infernally dull keeping the ledgers and cashing up every evening to make the books balance.

"At least the work is varied in the Army. We're off to Greenham Common later this morning, marching again, that'll get me away from my desk."

"Some of the lads are grumbling about the route marches. They think B-B is behind the times and hasn't heard about the new mechanised warfare with lorries and tanks."

"Well, his mind is set on the Great War," said Brian. "Trenches, shelling and all that stuff. But actually I think the marching's jolly useful. It's getting the men fit."

"That's the spirit," said Simon. "Are you going to classes this afternoon?"

"Not today." Brian took a slice of toast and began to butter it. "Ronnie's doing platoon tactics, so that's for the second lieutenants. Company commanders have been asked to attend on Friday for field engineering and strategy."

"I'm going to that one too," said Simon. "But I think we have both been over the ground before... at camp. You know, we're the old boys in the battalion now."

Brian was amused. Simon was one of the older officers, but Brian was just approaching his 23rd birthday. Besides, he had been the 'baby' of his family, the most junior clerk in the bank and, for many years, the youngest officer in the battalion. He had even found it difficult to grow a moustache. With so many new recruits, though, he must indeed be one of the old boys.

"Well, I got my commission in 1935 as soon as I left school. It's different for these lads who've only just joined us. Martin hardly looks old enough to shave. Do you think they'll let him go to France?"

"Oh, I think so," said Simon, getting up from the table. "He's 19 and that's the rule. Don't forget we've got to put on a good show for the top brass tomorrow." The battalion's two honorary colonels, Her Royal Highness the Duchess of Kent and Lord Cottesloe were coming to inspect them.

"Don't I know it. It's a damn nuisance. It's hard enough training the lads for war and then THEY come along and want to see us all spick and span. Some of my men haven't got boots yet and some are wearing their fathers' trousers and puttees from the Great War. They're a motley crew. I wish the clothing issue would come through."

"Not our fault, old chap. We must do the best we can with what we've got. I'm sure your men will look grand."

"I hear there's going to be a photograph," said Brian.

"Indeed. All the officers and the two honorary colonels, the Duchess in the middle of the front row, of course. A bit like a cricket team... or a school photo. It'll be a memento for us all." Simon raised his eyebrows. "After the war, we can frame it and hang it on our office walls." After the war seemed a lifetime away.

England, 2017

I lifted the lid of the old dark chest wondering what lurked inside. It stood in my parents' house, the repository of bits and pieces that 'might come in useful one day'. Every family has a place like that, a loft, a shed or a bottom drawer; for us, it was this heavy oak chest. But now it must go; we had sold the house. My sister Prue peered inside and retrieved a black and white photograph in a broken frame.

"Whatever is this?" I looked over her shoulder and my throat choked up. I saw a phoenix rising from the ashes. There they were, the officers from the Bucks Battalion, as young men, posing with the Duchess of Kent in her fur tippet.

"It's Dad's battalion," I said. "The 1st Bucks in September 1939." I'd seen a copy in the regimental museum, their fresh eager faces under hats that looked too large, like little boys dressing up.

"Where is he?" she said, her eyes scanning the rows for a youthful edition of our father.

"Look, that's him." I pointed to a short young man with a moustache. "He's standing behind the Duchess with his friend, Simon." He looked proud to be part of the battalion, part of the war as he went off on his big adventure. I remembered from my early childhood that he used to go to reunion dinners, to meet up with his Army friends. One year he came home cock-a-hoop because one of them had called him the 'Peter Pan of the Battalion'.

"Does that mean you're the 'Leader of the Lost Boys'?" I was pleased that I knew the story.

"No, it means I'm the little boy that didn't grow up. I've still got my hair while the others are going bald." He smiled as he turned the phrase over on his tongue.

"What did you do at your dinner?"

"Oh, we talked about the war and remembered." I was the post-war baby, the future my parents never thought they'd have. The war was over when I was born; I had missed it. I was curious, of course – children are. I had been told it was a 'Terrible Time' when bombs fell, men

were away and people got killed. But grown-ups were baffling. If the war had been such a 'Terrible Time', why did my father meet up with his friends to remember? Why did my mother and aunts talk about the things they had done in the war? When I asked questions, I didn't get answers or, if I did, I couldn't understand them. I felt I was groping through fog, my hearing muffled, my sight distorted.

Then my father decided not to go to any more reunions. He didn't want to be called Captain Dowling, didn't want to march with the British Legion on Remembrance Sunday, didn't want to remember any more.

"I won't glorify the war. It's behind us now. Time to move on." And he had; his marriage, his career, his children absorbed him. Yet he had kept the photo. As we sorted through the detritus of a life, the kaleidoscope turned and he emerged the Peter Pan of the Battalion once again.

CHAPTER 3

December 1939

The snow fell around Stone Cottage and the thin walls offered scant protection against the wild weather. Margery and Norah sat on the sofa by the fire, huddled round its flickering flames, their faces glowing and their legs tucked up under their skirts. They were old friends, bound together from girlhood by a shared sense of humour, a passion for horses… and by Johnnie. To Margery, he was just her brother but to Norah, he was a hero, her sweetheart, the love of her life. They heard the wind howl and saw the heavy curtains lift in the draught. Margery felt glad to have finished her shift and be home ahead of the first winter storm.

"How's Jack?" said Norah. She asked first about the important things, the horses.

"He's a bit bored, to tell the truth. There's hardly been any hunting and he doesn't get many rides. Johnnie's away and I'm busy at the hospital."

"Tell me about your work. I'm thinking of volunteering myself, if Mother will let me. Do you enjoy it?"

"Yes, on the whole. I like the patients and their stories – everyone's so different. The doctors and nurses from St Thomas's are a fun crowd and it's interesting to meet so many new people; it is a limited society in Slough." They had all grown up in Slough, Margery, Johnnie, Brian and Norah. "There's a lot of hard work too, scrubbing and polishing mainly, and no-one can enjoy emptying bedpans." Norah wrinkled her nose in disgust.

"And what about Betty's wedding. What's your bridesmaid's dress like?"

"Well, it's red brocade, with a fitted bodice and a full skirt." Margery threw another log on the fire. "And, as it's bound to be cold in the church on Boxing Day, there's a little fur cape to go over the top. I can take that off for the evening when there's going to be a dance."

"Lucky you. It's so exciting to have new clothes, especially when there's a war on. Why are they getting married on Boxing Day? I didn't know you could."

"John Armstrong has only got a couple of days' leave from his squadron. He needs to be back at his base by New Year's Eve."

"Right-ho. By the way, we saw a good film last night," said Norah. "I'm sorry you didn't come."

"I had no-one to go with and I'm tired of playing gooseberry with you and Johnnie. You were lucky that *he* had leave. Besides, I needed to wash my hair." Margery's long, thick hair was difficult to manage at the hospital; it kept slipping out from under her nurse's cap, and then she picked up head lice.

"I did enjoy it when we could do things as a foursome back in the summer."

"This Phoney War makes everything so dreary," said Margery. "All the boys have gone away, training to be soldiers, or pilots or something. It's not like it used to be – tennis parties, picnics, dancing – always something going on." She remembered those happy days ticking on one after another like golden beads on a necklace; she had thought they would go on forever. Could it be only five months since that ride, that tea party, that day of Brian's question?

As if reading her mind, Norah said: "What happened to Brian?"

"He went away to camp, of course." Margery tried to bring the conversation to a full stop but Norah hung on.

"Yes... but he has been home on leave. Johnnie and I have seen him several times in Slough but he didn't come here, did he? Yet you two were so close back in the summer."

"Yes, we were and I wanted it to go on like that, chums... but he wanted commitment."

"And you didn't?"

"I didn't..." Last summer seemed a different world, a world of friends, fun and parties. "But that was then; now I don't know. Everything has changed so much, Norah. I feel very... confused."

Margery tried to put a brave face on it but her voice wavered. She sniffed and reached up her sleeve for her handkerchief. She felt the ground shifting beneath her feet as if she could no longer be sure of anything. Back in July Brian had been perceptive; he had seen that their glorious summer days were ephemeral, like swallows, but she had been blithely unaware and now she pined for him.

"That's the lot," said Brian. "We can crack on now." He climbed on board the bus and took his seat, peering through the dim December light at the falling snow. The battalion had been on an overnight exercise on Salisbury Plain.

"I found the last two lads having a smoke behind the shed. It's hellish cold out there, I can tell you." Brian had lost the feeling in his fingers and his toes. He blew on his hands and stuck them under his greatcoat, noticing the smell of smoke and tobacco. "I'm longing for a good wash and shave, and a decent meal; food cooked over open fires is ruined, either burnt and smoky or raw and smoky." The officers laughed.

"I'll be glad to get back to the Mess," said Simon. "Two nights in a trench, with snow on the ground, proved damnably unpleasant. It must have been hell for the boys in the Great War, either freezing cold or up to your knees in mud."

"Do you really think it'll be like that again?" asked Martin, shaking back his thick dark hair. "Like the last war, I mean. Hitler's campaigns against Czechoslovakia and Poland went like lightening, *Blitzkrieg* they call it." Martin had been studying Modern Languages at Oxford when war broke out; he was almost a schoolboy.

"Hard to say," Simon said. "The Western Front is different from the East; the French have the Maginot Line, after all. We are probably better placed to stop the Germans than the Czechs and the Poles."

Brian felt proud to be part of the Bucks Battalion; they were a good crowd. Several of the officers had been up at Oxford, had travelled abroad and they spoke French and German, which might be handy. Elliot, from the local printing works, had followed his father into the battalion; it was a family tradition. He had helped Brian when he first joined up and he had confidence in Elliot but there seemed to be tension between him and the new boy, Brian Heyworth. He came from 'up north', a blunt plain-speaking man, with no shades of colour, no subtle hues; he seemed clever though, and he went down well with B-B.

"I expect there'll be some mail for us at the Mess," said Martin. "I'm waiting for a letter from Nancy."

Brian envied Martin his regular letters from his sweetheart. He knew *he* couldn't expect a letter from the person he cared most about; he'd finished with all that – except for the pain. His stomach clenched as he thought about it. He hadn't seen her in months; he had deliberately kept away. Best not to think about her, he decided.

"I hear there's a chance we'll get leave over Christmas," said Bill. "Ten days, they say."

"Could be," Simon said. "It all depends."

"Sounds like embarkation leave to me. You know 'Say goodbye to your nearest and dearest and then sail off to France in the New Year.'" They all laughed but Brian pondered these words as they trundled slowly along the icy roads. The snow outside drifted deep and dirty, piled up on the verges and large flakes fell again, like balls of cotton wool drifting against the windowpanes. His mood felt as sombre as the darkening countryside. 'Off to France in the New Year', going to war, to the frontline, to stand against Hitler's Army. Would he go without saying goodbye to Margery?

Christmas Day at Ditham Croft followed an unvarying pattern: church, lunch, the King's Speech, and finally present giving. Brian had arrived home the previous afternoon, to the delight of his mother, Amy. Brian thought she was like a hen with her chicks, gathering her family for the festival. Only Brian's brother, Bernard, was absent; this year he was spending the day with his wife's family. Brian noticed that Amy accepted – albeit reluctantly – that they had to take turns.

The family gathered in the dining room, dark with

heavy furniture. The thin warmth from the electric fire was insufficient to heat the room and Brian shivered as Frank, his father, said grace. They all sat on hard, upright chairs with their barley twist legs gathering around the large oak table bedecked with one sprig of holly. The turkey tasted rich and gamey, just as I like it, thought Brian. There were crispy roast potatoes, home-grown Brussels sprouts, carrots and bread sauce tasting of onions and cloves. Christmas pudding followed; it had been made by Amy back in October. Young John, Brian's nephew, needed a cushion to reach the table and was reluctant to try the pudding.

"Just a taste, darling," said his mother, Doris. "How do you know you don't like it, when you've never tried it?"

"When I was his age, I had to eat what we were given, with no fuss," said Hether, his name shortened from his surname: Hetherington. He was older than Doris and had been brought up in a strict Victorian regime. Brian realised he found it difficult to come to terms with modern fatherhood. John took a mouthful of pudding, turning it round in his mouth.

"There's something hard in it," he said.

"Let me see." Doris peered into his mouth. "You've found the silver threepenny bit."

"Lucky boy!" said his grandmother. "You are the only one who's found a coin. You can put that in your money box."

Afterwards, Brian lit a cigarette and took his seat to listen to the King. The message about peace struck a chord, tempered as it was by the King's conviction that *'we are fighting against wickedness'*. Those were his sentiments exactly.

"A truly Christian speech," said Frank.

"His radio addresses could be important in the war," said Hether. "He seems to be overcoming his stammer now."

Brian's thoughts turned to Margery, a 'Daddy's girl', who had suffered with a stammer after the sudden death of her father when she was just a child. He wondered whether she would be at the wedding tomorrow; after all, she was the bride's cousin. The thought of meeting her again made his heart race, gave him a queasy feeling. He hoped he could master his feelings and they could meet as chums but it wouldn't be easy, far from it.

Margery was a bridesmaid – the chief bridesmaid – and Brian watched as she stood at the front of the church and took the bouquet from her cousin for the service. Had she noticed him, sitting midway down the dark church with his parents? He thought she looked beautiful in her red bridesmaid's dress, like a peony or a poppy, but, to him, she always looked beautiful. His emotions rose stronger than ever now he saw her again. It's true, he thought, absence makes the heart grow fonder. How would she be when he spoke to her? Would she dance with him if he asked? His thoughts in turmoil, he rose with the rest of the guests to sing a hymn. When they left the church, Brian went over to speak to Johnnie and Nellie.

"Brian," said Nellie, holding out her gloved hands. "It's so long since we've seen you. What have you been up to?"

"I've been away training with the battalion, Mrs Street, drilling, route marches, night exercises, that sort of thing. There is a war on, you know." Everyone laughed at the familiar catch phrase. Margery came up behind him.

"Hello, Brian. I hope you're coming to the dance tonight."

"Margery, how nice to see you again. Yes, of course I'm coming tonight. I have to make the most of these last few days." There was no awkwardness; they fell back into their easy companionship with no defensiveness, no ill feeling. A bud of hope emerged; could it be...?

"How long's your leave?" asked Johnnie.

"Just ten days, and then we're off, but no-one's saying where at the moment."

"Sounds a bit ominous," said Johnnie, raising his eyebrows. Brian made no reply.

"Will you keep a dance for me this evening?" he asked Margery.

"Of course, I will. Several, in fact." That's encouraging Brian thought, as he turned back to his parents.

Later that evening, as the band played *Susie Woosie* in the ballroom, Brian and Margery waltzed together. He knew Margery loved dancing; she glided over the floor, a feather in his arms. He was a technical dancer; he knew the steps but his feet felt heavy, clumpy, made for marching not dancing. Margery chattered away about her work, her animals and their mutual friends, as they made their way around the dance floor moving from the tables on one side to the long blackout curtains which screened the windows.

"I thought you'd be engaged by now," he said, a teasing twinkle in his eye. "To someone like… Donald."

"Oh no, he's away in the Airforce and, besides, he's such a dull boy." Margery wrinkled her face and smiled at Brian. His heart felt lighter, his spirits rose and his stomach turned somersaults. He steered Margery towards the balcony and the two of them crept through the thick blackout curtains and away from the crowds and the dance floor.

"Look," she said. "There's a hunter's moon tonight."

"Or a lovers' moon." Brian took her in his arms and kissed her. To his joy, Margery kissed him back, as if she had been waiting for this moment.

"I've missed you. I didn't know how much I'd miss you until you weren't there," she said. Brian's heart soared and his head spun; these were the words he'd longed to hear.

"I was so worried you wouldn't come back. You saw Johnnie, but you stayed away from me for so long."

"I couldn't bear to come to Stone Cottage, to see you and to know that we were 'just chums'."

"I never realised how much you meant to me... until you had gone."

"If I were to ask you the question I asked last summer, would you give me a different answer?"

"Oh yes," she said. He held her close and, as the music drifted through the curtains, they danced on the balcony 'in the light of the silvery moon', their romantic moment, stolen from the dance, the wedding and the war.

CHAPTER 4

England, January 1940

The bell on the door tinkled as they burst into the jeweller's shop. Their cheeks glowed from the cold and from happiness. He removed his officer's cap and held the door for her; she wore a red beret and a camel hair coat, smiling up at him with shining eyes.

"What can I do for you today, Sir?" The jeweller stood behind the polished wooden counter and Margery thought it must be a common sight in his business, a young man, in uniform, and his sweetheart, rushing to get engaged before the war swept them apart. She felt a sense of urgency. Brian laid his cap on the counter and undid the buttons of his greatcoat.

"We would like to look at rings, please, engagement rings."

"May I offer my congratulations to you both." The jeweller turned to a cabinet behind the counter, retrieved the key from a chain on his waistcoat, unlocked it and produced two trays of rings.

"You choose, darling," Brian said. "It's your ring, after all. Which one do you like?" Margery's heart thumped. These last few days had passed like a flash; outings with Brian, visiting friends and relations, receiving their congratulations. It seemed like she was on a carousal, whirling round and round, until... Don't think about that, she told herself and she turned her attention to the rings.

"You must like it too, darling. Let's choose together." Shopping with Brian was a new situation and for such an important purchase, a ring to wear for the rest of her life.

She didn't know what he liked; they had not had time to discuss it. Did he want her to have a big ring, to wear like a trophy on her hand? They looked so grand, so formal, so grown up. Tentatively, she tried several on, one after the other, but they didn't feel right, didn't look right and they all were so expensive. She stood there dithering, uncomfortable with her uncertainty.

"I'm not sure." A small frown clouded her face. Would he think she was being fussy? After all, this was the best jewellers in Windsor; everyone came here for their rings – Betty and John, Doris and Hether, Jean and Charles. Surely, they too could find something here.

"I have some more, if Madam would like to see." The jeweller turned again to the locked cabinet and produced another tray, carefully replacing the first two.

"What about this one?" Brian pointed to a large ring in the centre. Margery tried it on, but it looked vulgar. She shook her head, looking at Brian, sensing his eagerness to put a ring on her finger… and they only had two more days. Where had the time gone?

Then she saw it, nestling at the back of the tray, a little ring with three stones, a small diamond, flanked by two sapphires. The jeweller passed it to her. She slid it onto her finger; it looked tasteful and elegant, and she loved the way the diamond sparkled in the light, like dancing fairies.

"Do you like this one?" Her green eyes shone as she held up her hand to Brian.

"It looks perfect on your hand, my sweet. But are you sure? Do you want to look at some more?"

"This is the one I like." Her face reflected her joy with the ring and with Brian. "But it doesn't fit very well. Look, it's a bit loose and I wouldn't want it to fall off."

"Can something be done about that?" Brian asked the jeweller.

"Of course, Sir. I can measure Madam's finger and get it remade. It will take about three weeks. It'll have to go away, you see."

"Oh, that's a pity," said Margery. "Your leave will be over by then."

"It can't be helped. I'll make all the arrangements and you can pick it up when it's ready. I'll look forward to seeing it on your finger next time I'm home… on my first leave."

Back in the Mess, Brian felt a different man. Had he only been away ten days? So much had happened, so much had changed. He felt as if he had lived an age in the twinkling of an eye, passed a milestone to enter an enchanted world. Never in his wildest dreams had he expected to return as Margery's fiancé. His leave had flashed by, the days over too quickly in an ecstatic whirlwind of togetherness. It seemed cruel that they couldn't have longer. Quietly, he told Simon his news.

"Well done, old boy! Best to get it settled before we go."

"When do you think we'll be off?"

"Pretty soon, I think. They're sending Bill to look for billets."

"Is it settled?" said Brian. "France? Or Scotland for more training?"

"I think we're done with training; it's the real thing this time. The King's coming to inspect us next week."

The news hit Brian like a blow in his stomach. He had been hoping for a delay, a stay of execution, a few weekends on leave to spend with Margery; but if the King was coming, that must mean they were off to France to serve 'King and Country'. Why, oh why, did it have to be now? Just when they had found each other at last. He mourned those weeks, months in the autumn, when he had kept away from her, time lost, never to be regained. Later that evening he rang her.

"I got back all right but the trains were slow. We spent two hours outside Didcot and it was cold in the carriage without heating or lights. I spent the time huddled under my greatcoat thinking of you. I miss you so."

"I miss you too. Do you think you might get home at the weekend?"

"I think that's unlikely. We've got to do a lot of packing but if you were able to come over for a day, I could perhaps wangle some time off. Might that be possible?"

"It all depends on my shifts. How would I get there?"

"Hether could wangle you some petrol, if you came by car, and that's the best plan because the trains are unreliable."

"I'll see what I can do."

Brian ached to see her again, to hold her in his arms, to feel her body against his. He had found some hairpins in his pocket and some stray dark hairs on his greatcoat. He remembered the time they had kissed in his little car and her hair had come down, thick, dark and glossy as he ran his fingers through its length. He relived those moments, hugging them close, turning them around in his mind.

On the day of the King's visit the frost on the parade ground was unremitting under their heavy boots, their fingers freezing as they left the Officers' Mess.

"He'd better make it snappy, or the men will get frostbite before they ever see the enemy," said Simon.

This inspection was different from the one in September with the Duchess of Kent. Brian's company were well turned out: they all had uniforms, equipment, and knew how to salute and present arms. They were a professional outfit, ready for action. The troops stood in the cold light of the January dawn, trying not to shiver as King George VI walked along their ranks. The royal visit was 'snappy'; he had been and gone before 10am.

"John, that's a terrible cough," said Brian to one of his lieutenants as they walked to the Mess together. John was tall and thin, another of their new recruits; he had the makings of a good officer.

"I feel wretched. I've got a raging sore throat and headache. Several of the lads in my platoon are in the same boat and it didn't do us much good, standing around for the King." Brian knew that laryngitis was rife; eight of the officers were suffering and about a third of the men.

"I think it's the fog," he told Margery later as he shivered in the phone box. "It smothers Newbury like a wet blanket."

"Will that stop you going?" croaked Margery. She was ill and Brian was worried; he longed to look after her.

"No, I don't think so, more's the pity."

"I'm feeling wretched, not well enough to come and see you tomorrow. Mum says I ought to be in bed"

"Mum's quite right. You must look after yourself, my sweet. I'm fine – except for missing you. I'll write when we get there." The pips sounded and Brian had no more coins.

Two days later, on 17th January 1940, Brian and the Bucks Battalion sailed for France.

CHAPTER 5

England, January 1940

The manure steamed in the frosty air as Margery mucked out the stables. This was her regular job before she went to work. She tied Jack up outside the stable to eat his feed, and put Joey onto his peg and chain at the end of the orchard. He was lucky to spend the day outside.

"You poor boy," she said to Jack. "No ride today, I'm afraid, but I'll make it up to you on my day off. I know your feed is mostly chaff and bran but you're lucky to have that." It took all Nellie's charm, plus a dozen eggs, to persuade Ernie at the mill to let them have a few oats; there were no rations for hunters. Jack was such a big horse, and not in his first youth either, but he meant so much to her, the first horse she had ever owned.

Margery felt that the war was just a game where they all dressed up, the boys as soldiers, the girls as nurses. The Phoney War they called it, no bombs, no fighting, just the blackout, rationing and Brian gone, like a rider in the mist. She went back to the kitchen and sat down to breakfast, a boiled egg with a piece of toast; bacon had become a rare treat now rationing had come in. She dawdled over her food, chewing every mouthful slowly, taking small sips of tea, her eyes fixed on the back door.

"Bert's late today."

"Not really," Nellie said. "It's often after nine before he gets here. You'd better get a move on or you're the one who'll be late, my girl."

"I suppose so." Margery moved to the door to fetch her

coat. Her head felt cloudy, her nerves on edge, nothing felt right. Perhaps she wasn't properly over the 'flu. She came in tying a scarf around her head.

"Postie here." Bert poked his head round the kitchen door. "I think I'll be in your good books today, Miss. I've got a letter for you. Field Post, it says, passed by the Censor and all."

"Oh Bert! Thank you." Margery tore open the tardy envelope and scanned the contents. She felt better already.

"He's fine." The tears streamed down her face. "They've arrived safely but he can't say where they are. It's freezing cold, so cold that the ink froze in his pen. Think of that, Mum. They're still on the move and not settled yet. Oh, he wants me to let his parents know he's arrived. Could you give them a ring, Mum? I'm already late. Tell them we'll call in on Thursday when we go to pick up the ring."

She popped the letter in her coat pocket as she fetched her bike from the garage. She pedalled until her legs hurt to make up for lost time. Her heart sang and her spirits soared; Brian still loved her, he said so. He told her to remember how much they had to look forward to, their whole lives together. That was a good thought, something to hold onto until his first leave.

On Thursday, the jeweller had the ring ready when they called to collect it. Margery smiled as she put it on her finger; it fitted beautifully, linking her to Brian, their memories and their future. Margery and Nellie had been invited for tea at Ditham Croft and they made sure they arrived on time; Amy was a stickler for punctuality. Margery found Brian's parents intimidating; their strict routines, their unspoken rules made her feel an outsider. The Dowlings were a secret society to which she had to earn admittance; but she didn't know the password... not yet.

Nellie rang the bell and Brian's sister Brenda opened the door; she had been at school with Margery, a prefect when Margery was only in the Remove. Her fair curls, merry eyes and clear complexion had won her the part of the Fairy Godmother in the Christmas pantomime. She was petite, like a pretty little bird.

"It's so exciting, you and Brian." Brenda came forward, took both her hands and kissed Margery on the cheek. "Do show me the ring."

Margery drew off her gloves and the diamond sparkled in the light.

"How sweet!" Brenda said. "We're going to be sisters. I know we'll have such fun."

Margery felt better already. Brian's parents came into the hall. Amy was a tiny woman with her iron grey hair scraped back into a bun; Frank had a bald head fringed by white hair and kind, twinkling eyes. They seemed older than Nellie as they bent to admire the ring, in their own fashion.

"Very appropriate, my dear," said Frank. "A pretty little ring."

"Brian always did have good taste," Amy sniffed. Margery wondered if that meant she didn't. Was it her fault that Amy was so stiff? Would she ever accept her as good enough for Brian? Frank turned to greet Nellie.

"Come in by the fire, Mrs Street. It's a cold day and it gets dark early. Of course, January's such a long month." Frank and Amy were pleased that Margery had brought Brian's letter and, after tea, they listened while she read it out – at least, she read out those parts which were meant for sharing; the rest she hugged to herself, like hidden treasure. Nellie made small talk about their families, their mutual friends in Slough, the difficulties of rationing and the tea party passed well enough. Another step in family bonding, Margery thought.

France, February 1940

"How's your billet?" Brian asked. He and Bill had been sent on an attachment to the British sector of the Saar, to see the defences and get experience with a Regular Army unit. They drove out of the small mining town along a straight road with poplar trees lining the verges like a guard of honour.

"Not bad, except for the sanitation, the 'bucket and chuck it' variety," Bill said. Brian chuckled, his mind going back to the wizened old couple who lived down the end of Margery's road. Noah and Sarah, wasn't it? Something biblical anyway. They too had no 'facilities', but they grew lovely roses. He couldn't imagine roses blooming in the sad little town where they were billeted; it seemed a place forgotten, left from some bygone age. The roads were cobbled, the slag heaps cast shadows, like death's fingers, and worst of all was the smoke, thick smoke blackening the air, the houses, the washing and the people.

Simon and Brian were billeted together. It was all right, as these things went, but none of the houses had bathrooms; the troops made weekly visits to the bathhouse, taking it in turns. Brian always felt more civlilised after his bath, as if he'd rejoined the human race. He supposed it was because he took cleanliness for granted whereas the French didn't seem to worry; a visit to the bathhouse at Christmas and Easter was enough for them. They didn't notice their surroundings either, the smoke, the grime, the condition of the buildings.

"The lads in my company have worked so hard to make that old factory into habitable billets," said Brian. "They've used bits of old timber and scrap metal to make latrine buckets, table tops, and washing up bowls and, Bob's your uncle, they've got a cosy place."

The countryside looked so different from England and it was such fun, so foreign, driving on the right-hand side of the road, the French cheeses, the long loaves of bread and the houses with shutters at the windows. If only Margery sat beside him, it would be just perfect. They would find a grand place for a picnic in this flat open countryside, over by that little wood maybe. He would have so much to tell her when he saw her again; there was so much he couldn't say in his letters. He must make a list, ready for his leave. His turn would come in May and he wanted to get married while he was home. He was chuffed to bits about his engagement and hoped she'd see the sense in an early wedding; he ached as he longed to touch her, stroke her, kiss her.

"These cobbled roads play hell with my feet, marching along them," said Bill, breaking into his thoughts.

"Tell me about it."

"I'm glad we've got a few days away from the battalion and censoring those endless letters."

"Some of the lads seem to write to everyone in Buckinghamshire. They're just too damned literate." Brian was glad no-one else was reading his letters; his job as a censor made him feel like a peeping Tom. It had been hard recently as the officers had been a bit thin on the ground; some had gone on courses and some had had 'flu.

"Have you had the 'flu?" asked Bill.

"I was lucky; I escaped lightly. Just a day in bed and a bit of a cough. Not like poor B-B." Their colonel had been invalided back to England. "I'm chuffed Ronnie's taken over. I've got a lot of confidence in him. He's a good trainer."

"He pushes you but I like being stretched, and he always makes you feel you can come up to the mark."

Brian agreed but he knew that Ronnie had never seen active service. That's why they were going on this assignment, to talk to Regular Army officers and see the Maginot Line. They both knew the plan; a strong defence along the Franco-German border with state-of-the-art concrete bunkers, impenetrable but with good living conditions for the troops. Brian knew the British would have to start digging when the ground thawed; they needed trenches and anti-tank ditches to complete the line of defence right up to Dunkirk and the Channel. He wanted to get ideas from the Maginot Line and, although he knew they could never produce anything so grand, he was confident they could do enough to stop Hitler's advance. They'd hold the line when the time came, he was sure of it.

England, February 1940

Fleda cranked the starting handle. The engine caught, spluttered... and then died. There was a strong smell of petrol as she tried again; this time it settled into a steady chug, chug, chug and Margery heaved a sigh of relief. A lift home from the hospital made a welcome change from her bicycle and she watched the weak sunshine filtering through the bare branches of the oak trees.

"How are you finding the work, Fleda?"

"It's not bad. Going around from ward to ward with the trolley makes for variety and I meet lots of people but the discipline's a bit constraining. It's like a corset; you're pushed this way and that with very little freedom to manoeuvre."

"You're a scream, Fleda."

"I'm dying to hear about your wedding plans, Margery. How's it all going?" Fleda gripped the steering wheel as the car leapt towards the hedge.

"Oh all right, I suppose." Margery heaved a sigh as she looked out of the window. The verges were bare; it was still too cold for primroses. She didn't want to talk about the wedding but Fleda persisted.

"How will you manage for a wedding cake? Charles and Eileen had iced a cardboard box with a tiny cake inside."

"Mum's friend is taking care of it. She has a restaurant and they can still get supplies; it'll be their wedding gift." Margery knew she should be excited but she wasn't; she just felt muddled. She knew she wanted to marry Brian but she wasn't sure whether she wanted to rush into it on his first leave. Still, he was dead set on it so she thought she'd better go along with it.

"What's the matter, Margery? You're usually so upbeat."

"It's hard being away from Brian. His mother thinks we're far too young to get married and, besides, I'm sure she disapproves of me." Fleda gave a toss of her head and a sniff, imitating Amy.

"She's a miserable old besom but she's not the bride. What do *you* want to do?"

"I'm not sure, that's the trouble. Marriage is such a big step. It's different for Brian. He'll go back to France and everything will go on much the same but for me my whole life will change." Margery loved her job, caring for the patients, meeting new people, going out with the student doctors; it gave her a taste of independence. She was worried that Brian might want her to stop working once they were married, and there were loads of other issues, like where they'd live, his family, whether to have children and so on. It all seemed too much.

"Mmm, I see. With Brian away you'll have all the constraints of being a married woman but none of the wedded bliss." Fleda winked and Margery hung her head. She was not used to making decisions. Maybe she should wait? Brian would have leave again in the autumn and they could get married then. But, would he be dreadfully disappointed? She wished he was home so they could sit side by side and talk it through; she was sure she'd be able to make up her mind if he were there.

CHAPTER 6

France, March 1940

Brian looked around the *Grand Place*, its tall Flemish buildings dominating the skyline. The architecture was too heavy for his taste, too forbidding; he preferred cleaner lines, like Windsor or London.

"That's *La Vieille Bourse*," said Simon. "The Stock Exchange." Both of them had been bankers in civvy street in that bygone age before the war. Brian wondered whether he would ever go back to the bank. Army life seemed more exciting and he might apply for a regular commision when the war was over.

"It is grand to be back in civilisation," said Brian. It was their first 'jaunt', an outing away from the base. There had been so much to do since they came to France, setting up, digging trenches, censoring letters, firing practice, court martials and, of course, church parades on Sundays. The French all turned out to watch the band play as the troops marched down the main street in Wahagnies to the town square, with the church on one side and the *Mairie* on the other. The battalion put on a magnificent show, worthy of the guards, Brian thought.

Brian and Simon had come to Lille to buy clocks for the billets and material to make bunting for the children's party on Easter Monday. Once those errands had been completed, they gave themselves the rest of the day off; it was Easter Saturday, after all and they set off to see the sights.

"First things first, old boy," said Simon who had been in France before the war. "We must find a café and sit on the pavement with a cup of coffee and a croissant, if such things can be had in wartime. Then we'll see what else this town has to offer." They chose a café on the *Grand Place*, sat themselves at a table and ordered two coffees.

"Je suis desolée, Messieurs. C'est interdit," said the waitress but other people were being served; they were confused. The waitress explained that she was forbidden to serve troops before six thirty. What a disappointment!

"Change of plan, then," said Simon. "Sightseeing first, then coffee." So they walked around the town like tourists, looked at the shops and went into the church. Brian was intrigued by the wooden booths up the side aisles; he had never seen these in English churches.

"It's for Confession," Simon said. "They're all Catholics, you see. There's nothing to detain us here. I suggest we visit that hairdressers we saw in the last street."

Brian removed his cap and ran his hand over his fair curls; he could do with a decent haircut. Two hours later, they emerged once more into the *Grand Place*.

"Time for a drink, now," said Simon. "I feel like something more than a coffee."

"So do I," said Brian. Once again, they settled themselves at a table and asked for an aperitif.

"Je suis desolée, Messieurs. C'est interdit," said the waitress. It seemed like a refrain, all she could say.

"Pourquoi?" said Brian in his hesitant schoolboy French. He looked at his watch. *"C'est apres six heures et demi."*

"Oui, Monsieur. Mais aujourdui, les aperitifs sont interdit," It was French rationing, no aperitifs on certain days of the month and Easter Saturday was a dry day.

"Alors, deux cafés au lait, s'il vous plait," said Simon. "At least we can sit here and watch the world go by. Those ladies' Easter bonnets look amusing. Have you seen that one with the bird peeping out? I wonder if that's the new fashion? Do you think the girls at home are wearing them?"

"Maybe, but I can't see Margery in anything like that."

"Nor Jane. She's finding it difficult with me in France when there's a baby on the way. I'm looking forward to leave so I can cheer her up. Tell me, how did you meet Margery?"

"Oh, we've known each other forever. Our families were acquainted and I went to kindergarten with her brother. We were always in and out of each other's houses, you know how it is, and Margery would be hanging around us boys but I didn't take much notice. Then in the last few years, we all started to do things in a group; I'd go along as Johnnie's friend and Margery would bring another girl and we'd play tennis, go to the flicks, go for a run in my little car, that sort of thing. That's when I really began to notice her. She seemed different from other girls. She's such fun and she seemed so vivid... and I fell in love."

"You're a lucky man judging by that photo you've got beside your bed. She looks a grand girl."

"Yes and we're going to get married on my first leave. I can hardly wait. I say, time's getting on. Shall we look for somewhere to eat?"

"That's a good idea. I don't know about you but I'd much prefer to find some little family-run place in the backstreets where they value their cooking. I don't want to go to that hotel we saw in the main square where we'll eat indifferent food in the company of every other British officer in town." Simon's French was better than Brian's and he asked a passing French officer for a recommendation. They found the restaurant easily and it was frequented by middle class French couples.

"It's always a good sign when the locals eat in a place," said Simon. Brian was enchanted by the atmosphere, the smell of garlic and the people; there was a young woman with lurid red hair, and a toy poodle whose coat was dyed a similar shade. Brian thought she gave the place some true continental glamour.

"It's a distinctively French menu, handwritten and almost illegible," said Simon. "Shall we start with soup? It's leek and potato, so we can't go far wrong with that. Then there's a choice of chicken, fish or pork. Which do you fancy?"

"I'll have the chicken and what about vegetables?"

"Nothing much in that line, just potatoes and maybe a bit of cabbage if we're lucky but the wine list looks good. Shall we go for champagne as we're in the region?"

"Sounds a good idea. I wish I could take some home for my wedding. It's devilish difficult to get it at home and a wedding without champagne sounds pretty tame to me."

The meal was served at a pace that gave them time to savour each dish and wash it down with the excellent champagne. Soon one bottle became two and Brian's head spun as his body defied gravity. He leaned on Simon as they weaved their way back to the car.

"Time for a little choir practice, I think," said Simon. "We've got to sing *La Marseillaise* for the children on Monday, remember?"

"Do you know the words, old boy? I always get a bit lost after *'Allons, enfants de la patrie'*."

"Never mind. Just la-la when you're unsure." They sang at the tops of their voices, as the car rolled along. They started with *La Marseillaise* and progressed to *Roll Out the Barrel, Pack Up Your Troubles in Your Old Kitbag* and the other favourites. They were young men, wined and dined, with their lives ahead of them; they felt invincible, indestructible.

The officers decorated the hall, hanging bunting and draping the Union Jack and *Le Tricoleur* for the Easter Monday tea party. The children of Wahagnies had been invited as the battalion's thank you to the local people for hosting them.

"*Gauche, gauche, gauche, droit, gauche,*" said *Monsieur le Professeur,* the schoolmaster. The boots battered and the clogs clattered as the children marched into the hall, each one clutching a ticket. Their knees were bare, their shorts and skirts frayed, but their faces shone and their hair had been slicked down for the occasion.

"They look such happy little fellows," said Brian.

"Let's get going. What's the plan?" Major Heyworth didn't want to waste time.

"A couple of games of Musical Bumps and then the cine show," said Elliot.

"Crack on, then."

Brian thought Heyworth sounded impatient. The children ran about, this way and that, like swallows in the evening light. They vied with each other to sit down with a plop when the music stopped. This is just the job to work off those high spirits, thought Brian. There were prizes for the winners, presented by Major Heyworth.

"Qu'est-ce que c'est?" the children shouted, crowding round the lucky winners as they unwrapped miniature Union Jacks. They're just like the ones we used to put on our sandcastles, thought Brian, his mind, as ever, drifting back to Margery and the childhood holidays they had spent together at Sandbanks.

"Asseyez vous! Asseyez vous!" shouted Martin. Languages come in useful, thought Brian, as the children, red-faced with exercise, settled down cross-legged on the floor. The officers had rigged up a screen, borrowed a projector and some films for the occasion.

"You can't go wrong with Mickey Mouse and Charlie Chaplin," said Simon. The children watched the slapstick and the officers watched the children. It was a rare treat; some of them had children of their own, some, like Brian, had nephews and nieces and their hearts warmed as they saw the little ones enjoying the simple humour until... the projector broke down.

"It's conked out," said David, their amateur projectionist.

"Buck up and fix it," said Heyworth as the children began to fidget and whisper amongst themselves, like birds preparing for flight.

"Wind it on a bit, old boy, and see that if does the trick," said Elliot.

It didn't. Black smoke began to emerge and David started coughing; the smell of burning made Brian's eyes smart. The officers reached for their handkerchiefs while the children wiped their faces on their sleeves.

"It's no good," said Elliot. "Best to crack on and have tea."

After tea, the battalion's mouth organ band played and they all sang. Then it was time for Pass the Parcel before the finale. The French children, directed by *Monsieur le Professeur,* sang *God Save the King* and then the officers sang *La Marseillaise.* The children lined up and were each given an Easter egg and an *Entente Cordiale* badge as they marched out, crumpled and flushed with bonhomie.

Brian walked into the Mess and picked up his letters, one from Brenda and one from Margery. He opened Margery's, his heart beating wildly as it always did at the sight of her writing. The letters were their intimate space, the thread uniting them. He read the first lines and felt as if he'd been kicked in the teeth. He had been pinning his hopes on an early marriage and he thought they had got it all sorted; he had been thrilled just thinking about the wedding, and the honeymoon but now Margery was holding back. Damned, he thought, why does she have to shilly-shally?

He kicked the ground as he went to inspect the trenches that his company were digging. That was the job now – digging the Gort Line – defensive trenches along the Franco-Belgian border. He came to the first platoon working with John and he noticed the men standing around, leaning on their shovels.

"What's happening here, John?"

"I'm just giving the lads a rest. The ground's heavy and it's hard work."

"We can't help that," said Brian. "You'll have to get a move on, as quick as you can or we'll have Hitler here before you've finished."

He had expected them to be further forward; they'd have to step on it now. Last year John had been studying

Philosophy at Oxford, a head in the clouds type, Brian thought, and far too lenient with the lads; they needed discipline. He strode away towards the next group where Corporal West was in charge.

"How's it going, West?"

"All right but we ran into a damp patch down there by the hedge so we moved the line a bit." Brian looked at the trenches and compared them with the plans.

"You did what, Corporal?" he said. "Your orders were to follow these plans – exactly."

"Yes Sir but…"

"No buts," said Brian. "You dig where you're told to dig. Our line has got to meet up with the Glosters. We can't have you deciding where to dig; orders are orders. You should know that by now."

"Yes, Sir."

Brian clenched his fists as he strode away. West had been so stupid. He had thought the lad had shaped up well and learned the ropes. He felt disappointed to find he'd been so slack; mistakes could cost lives. *His* men needed to take their soldiering seriously, to be 120 per cent efficient at all times. West's behaviour seemed a personal affront.

That evening, Brian sat at the table in his billet while Simon was already in bed. It had been a bad day. West had been wrong but Brian knew he had over-reacted. He should have handled it better; that was an officer's job. Margery's letter, her deferral letter, had upset him, disappointed him. He had been looking forward to the wedding so much. Marrying Margery seemed like a dream come true – except that now it wasn't going to happen anytime soon.

He ran his hand through his hair. Simon was asleep by

the looks of it. He always slept on his front with his face on the bolster. Funny that; Brian slept on his side. Perhaps he'd got this business with Margery out of proportion. After all, it was a girl's privilege to change her mind and she only asked him to wait a bit. She hadn't dismissed him, not like last summer. No, she still loved him, she said so. She was right, they were both very young and there would be other leaves.

He needed to put a brave face on it; sulking did no good. He wished he could talk to Margery as they'd soon clear this up face to face; but he couldn't. Letters took so long to come through and he'd better send a cheerful reply, telling her it was fine. He would act as if he didn't mind and say how much he looked forward to one leave as an engaged couple. That was the right thing to do; he knew that now.

CHAPTER 7

England, March 1940

Margery stood in the sluice room with her friend Peggy, scrubbing bedpans.

"It's funny, isn't it?" said Margery. "However much disinfectant you use it never gets rid of the smell. It's making me feel sick."

"It is a bit overpowering," said Peggy. "But it's Matron's orders: every bit of equipment to be scrubbed and polished, ready for action. We need to clear the decks." Peggy's voice seemed strident, discordant in the bare room and Margery's temples throbbed.

"We sent Mr Jackson home yesterday, although I think we would usually have kept him in another couple of days."

"We need to be ready when Hitler starts something." The Phoney War had gone on for so long that Margery had got used to it. But now the climate had changed; everyone talked of a Spring Offensive and Margery was worried. What if Hitler did attack, and Brian's battalion was in the front line? He might be wounded... or worse. Perhaps they should get married as soon as possible. Why couldn't she make up her mind once and for all? Everything took on a different dimension if the Phoney War were to end and the real thing begin. Her thoughts kept spinning round and round; it was giving her a headache. Brian had been right last summer; the war had changed their lives. Maybe he was right again and she'd better settle for a wedding in May, on his first leave.

"By the way, did you have a good time last night?" said Peggy.

"Oh yes. I enjoyed it all. Do you know what those doctors from St Thomas's call us VADs?... the Glamour Girls. Isn't it a scream? I loved the dancing. Peter dances so well."

"You two seemed to have a lot to talk about," said Peggy. "Has Brian got competition?"

"No. We're just friends. He was telling me about South Africa. Brian thinks he might stay in the Army after the war and we might go there together." Brian had said that he was enjoying France and he'd like to see the world with Margery – after they'd settled Hitler, of course.

"I had a lovely evening," said Margery. "But I seem to be paying for it this morning. I don't usually feel this bad." She shook her head and rubbed her eyes; no doubt about it, she felt under the weather.

"Is Matron going to give you time off when Brian comes home?"

"Yes, she's agreed at last. Perhaps she is a human being after all." Margery had been caught between two opposing forces, Brian and Matron. Brian had been quietly determined that she should be free for his leave while Matron had said that the war effort must come first. Brian had said she should resign if Matron refused her request, but Margery loved her job. She hadn't known which way to turn and was glad it was settled.

"You're too good to lose," said Peggy. "They need VADs who work hard and keep at it, especially if it all kicks off and we get loads of casualties coming in. Does Brian mind you going out to dances and that when he's not here?"

"No. He says I should enjoy myself, when I get the chance. But my Mum's not so pleased. It's not right in her book."

“Old people have these funny ideas.” Peggy’s laugh echoed round the bare walls of the sluice room and Margery’s head thumped worse than ever; she wished her hangover would wear off. Her throat was sore too and her arms felt itchy.

By the end of the day, Margery felt as if she was walking through mud, sticky wet mud. Her legs felt heavy and her skin prickled as if she’d been stung by nettles. It was all she could do to ride her bike home, stagger into the kitchen and sink down on a chair by the table. Nellie put her hand on Margery’s forehead.

“Bed for you, my girl, right now. I’ll come along in a minute with a couple of aspirin and the thermometer.” Margery felt glad to rest her head on the pillow as the cool sheets eased her burning skin. The smell of lavendar took her back to childhood as Nellie put her hand on her pulse and popped the thermometer under her tongue.

“101°,” said Nellie. “Well above normal. Now let me have a look at you.” One glance at Margery’s flushed skin was enough for Nellie; she’d been a children’s nurse and had seen those spots before. “It’s German Measles, no doubt about it. You’ll have to stay in bed for a few days at least.”

“Oh Mum, it can’t be German Measles. That’s for children.”

“Well, you’ve never had it and now you’ve got it. The best place for you is bed. Besides, you’re infectious.”

France, April 1940

A strange smell greeted Brian as he walked into the Officers’ Mess. Brie, Camembert and Rochefort stood ripening on the shelf and, in the warm weather, the Camembert was particularly pungent. Brian walked across the bare room to fetch his food and sat down by Bill.

"What was it like the other day, driving the Duke around?" As Commanding Officer of HQ Company, it had been Brian's job to act as driver for the Duke of Gloucester when he came to visit the front line.

"It was rather fun, actually. He was a very pleasant fellow. I took him out to see the trenches, the concrete pill-boxes and the anti-tank ditches. He was very interested in it all. I found him easy to talk to and quite amusing. He spent a lot of time chatting to the lads and asking questions about what they were doing. It gave them a boost to talk to a Duke, something to write home about."

"And more letters in the pile for us to read," said Simon, reaching for the butter.

Brian was beginning to feel comfortable in France. The townspeople, suspicious of foreigners at first, had accepted them and, since the party, the children followed the officers everywhere. The battalion had established a routine and Brian felt settled.

"By the way, have you been on any of Bruce's tours?" said Bill. "You know the ones around the Great War battlefields?"

"I haven't been yet but I hear they're good. Bruce's always full of ideas and information. I want to give it a try, this Sunday perhaps."

"Sounds a bit morbid to me," said Simon.

"I'd like to see the countryside now the weather's getting warmer," said Brian. April was true to form, sunshine and showers. In the woods, the primroses were uncurling, bright little stars hiding in the grass, and on the birch trees a light green fuzz was drifting softly across the twigs. The longer days were warming the earth and the miners were planting vegetables. Brian no longer needed to wear his scarf and gloves as he inspected the trenches.

"They say it's good campaign weather," said Bill.

"We might see a lot more of battlefields soon, if Hitler starts a Spring Offensive," said Simon.

"Here's a letter for you, Brian," said John. Brian reached for his letter, turning it over in his hand. I'm glad she's written again so quickly, he thought, as he slit the envelope and started to read. Outside a blackbird sang, the soft notes drifting through the window. His heart leapt; he wanted to run and shout. She's changed her mind – again. She wants to get married on my first leave. That's just perfect. Hurrah, hurrah!

But then he remembered; he'd posted his reply, the one that said he looked forward to one leave as an engaged couple. Bother, oh bother; it would be well on its way by now. Damn these postal delays! Their letters must have crossed in the post. It took too long for letters to get through when you were so much in love. What if she thought *he* wanted to delay now? But, if he were to write another letter, their letters might cross again. What a muddle! How could he sort it out so she could see he definitely wanted a wedding on his first leave?

England, April 1940

Margery was still in quarantine but she felt much better. She went down the garden to feed the hens. They clucked in delight as she spread the potato peelings and cabbage leaves along their trough. They squawked and squabbled, scurrying around to peck up their share. This is a good place for hens, Margery thought; their pen is well screened behind these rhododendrons. She looked at their fat buds, bursting with promise; they'll be in bloom when Brian gets home, she thought. She heard footsteps coming along the path, urgent footsteps too quick for Nellie. Bert, the postman, stood by the gate, his face grave.

"Bert, it's a funny time for you, isn't it?"

"Miss, your mum's in a bit of a state. I've brought a telegram, you see… from France." Margery's hand shot to her chest and she clutched at her cardigan.

"Best come quick, Miss."

Bert stood aside to let her pass and Margery ran up the path. She knew telegrams spelled disaster. Nellie's brother had been killed in the Great War and a telegram had brought the news. Surely nothing could have happened to Brian? Margery rushed into the kitchen where Nellie stood, ashen faced, holding the small pink envelope.

"Do be quick, girl. Open it."

Margery's heart thudded and she sank into the nearest chair, her cheeks flushed, her hands trembling as she ripped open the envelope. She drew out the brown slip and struggled to make sense of the cryptic message. After a few minutes silence, she looked up, her eyes shining and her face relaxed.

"What is it? Is he all right?"

"Yes, Mum. He's fine. He just wanted to let me know that he agrees with my decision that we should get married on his first leave. Look." She spread out the typewritten form on the table.

"Oh, what a relief," said Nellie, tears streaming down her face. "I've been in such a state thinking something dreadful had happened to him. I've known him so long that he almost feels like one of mine." She sat down heavily in the nearest chair and lit a cigarette. "He's a naughty boy though to give me such a fright. I'm going to write to him and tick him off." They both laughed with relief.

"Now we must get down to business," said Margery. "We'll need to send out the invitations, talk to the Vicar, sort out the wedding cake, the whole works. He could be home in six weeks' time." Her head was full of plans; it was good to have settled it at last.

CHAPTER 8

France, April 1940

"So this is where you're hiding." Simon came striding into Brian's office, a bare room with a cluttered table for a desk. The latest reports showed that Hitler had walked into Norway and established a puppet regime. Brian was disappointed that the Navy hadn't been able to stop him. Now Hitler was turning west and intelligence reports showed that his troops were gathering on the Belgian border. Brian felt tension in the air, tightening the muscles in his neck, making it hard to sleep at night. Something must happen soon; this was perfect campaign weather.

"Be a good chap and hop along to the station, would you?" said Simon. "We've had a telegram to say there's someone arriving on the afternoon train who needs to be met by a senior officer. Take the car. It's just outside."

"Sounds like the Duke of Gloucester again." Brian stubbed out his cigarette and gathered his cap.

As he drove to the station Brian thought of Margery. Her letters were full of the preparations for the wedding, his wedding, their wedding. She had an appointment with the Vicar. Thank goodness, leave was going ahead; the first party were to go next week. He must get hold of a hymn book to suggest a hymn for the service but there was always so much to do: rotas for anti-parachute duty, court martials for petty offences, forms for equipment, his work seemed endless. It wasn't just the regular work; unexpected tasks turned up too, like this little jaunt. He realised that he didn't know whom he had been sent to meet. Simon hadn't said –

perhaps he didn't even know; it could be like that sometimes.

He parked the car outside the station. A whistle shrilled as the train came in, with a whoosh of steam which hung under the station roof. And there, walking through the smoke, Brian recognised his mystery passenger. It was their colonel, old B-B himself.

That was a surprise – and a shock. B-B had been away since January, sent home at the height of the 'flu epidemic in the days of icy breath and freezing ink. He had left them as a raw band of weekend soldiers, goggle-eyed at the French and their 'foreign' ways whereas now they had become an effective front line battalion, taking their soldiering seriously and confident they could hold the line when the Germans came. In B-B's absence, Ronnie had trained them well and they all had confidence in him. Was it wise for B-B to come back? But that's not my business, Brian thought, pulling himself together as he came to attention and saluted.

"Good to see you, Sir." He opened the passenger door. "I hope you're fully recovered."

"Yes, yes, my boy. Fighting fit now, fighting fit." Mmm, thought Brian, we'll see about that.

"I hope those damned nightingales don't keep us awake again tonight," said Simon as they went to their room.

"They say they sing to mark their territory." Brian sat on the bed to take off his shoes. "It's a bit like us really, sitting here protecting our loved ones from unwanted intruders."

"But we don't sing."

"I would if I thought it'd help." Brian knew there were worries about equipment, about transport, about the French forces… and about the Germans, massing on the border.

"I hope nothing happens till after we come back from leave." Brian's chest felt tense and his stomach tightened just thinking about the alternative. "I'm so looking forward to our wedding. I can hardly wait."

"Yes, I'll be glad to see Jane. She's over half way along now."

They felt they were in a race against time. They knew the Germans would come soon and, although they were desperate for leave, they didn't want to miss the show. If only Hitler would wait until after they'd had their turn, but it wasn't up to them; they knew that.

Ronnie, their acting colonel, had gone back to England when B-B returned and Brian missed him. He had trained them so well.

"How do you think B-B is getting on?" Brian was concerned that he was not fully fit; his colour was high, he tired easily and walked with a stick.

"He wants to be with us, that's clear. We're his boys and he feels he should be here. If determination can do it, he'll win through." Simon saw a great deal of their colonel.

Brian got into bed and listened to the nightingale, the notes trilling though the night air. If Margery were here and we heard him together, it'd be just perfect, he thought. I've not long to wait now, just four weeks and then we can be promised to each other for the rest of our lives.

CHAPTER 9

England, April 1940

"Light the fire, would you Johnnie," said Nellie. The old cottage felt damp, even though it was spring and Nellie drew the thick curtain across the middle of the room. "I think Margery's plain exhausted. First it was the German Measles, then she's got this wedding to organise and she's so busy at the hospital with the casualties coming in from Norway. You won't have to go, will you, Johnnie?"

"To Norway? Doesn't look like it Mum, but I *am* a soldier and there is a war on. I'll have to go somewhere soon – France, or Italy perhaps if Mussolini decides to join in." Nellie wrung her hands and frowned as Margery walked into the room.

"Are the spots all gone now, Curly Whirly?" Johnnie smirked and Margery threw a cushion at him. "Childish, childlish." He wagged his finger. "Only little girls throw cushions and only little girls get German Measles."

"Oh do shut up. I've got enough to do without you teasing me." Since Brian's telegram, Margery's lists seemed endless, book the Village Hall, buy the ring, order the cake, sort out her trousseau, go and see the Vicar; she had thrown herself into the arrangements, certain now about the wedding but Johnnie did annoy her. "Haven't you got anything better to do?" she said.

"Well, I have got a best man's speech to write." He scratched his head and yawned. "I hear there's going to be a wedding."

"Have you thought about what you're going to say?" said Nellie. "Nothing too rude now."

"Well, the usual way to start is to say how bride and groom met each other, 'one look was all it took', you know the sort of thing. But I can't do that 'cos they've known each other since birth. '*He* looked into *her* pram and it was love at first sight' doesn't sound quite right. Bit of a poser really." Margery laughed. Johnnie might be annoying but he could always cheer her up.

"You could say something about times you shared as children," said Nellie. "Holidays at Heathermead and Sandbanks, picnics in Windsor Forest."

"That's a good idea. Perhaps I'll tell the story about when he came down to Sandbanks on the dicky seat of Dad's car. He ate so much chocolate that he was sick into Margery's sand hole as soon as he got there. And what did she do? No sympathy: she just passed him the spade and told him to dig it out!"

"Mmm," said Nellie. "I don't think that's a good idea. Mr and Mrs Dowling wouldn't approve."

"Whoops, I'd forgotten they'd be there."

"Well, they are his parents, you know."

Margery drew in her breath and covered her face with her hands. She didn't want to upset her new family but Johnnie knew them better than she did; he'd been in and out of their house since he was a boy.

"No, you're quite right. Brian overindulging is not really their cup of tea," he said. "And talking of cups of tea, it's not going to be a 'dry' party is it? Weddings and champagne always seem to go together, a sort of magic combination."

"Yes, we've sorted out the champagne. Brian's in champagne country but he can't bring any back. He knows

Mum can't pay for it all so the champagne is to be his contribution. He's sent me a blank cheque."

"Good man."

"Has he sent you his guest list yet?" said Nellie. "We need to know who he wants to invite on the Dowling side."

"It's coming, but it's going via his parents first so they can fill in some of the addresses."

Margery propped her bike by the Vicarage gate and smoothed down her cotton frock. Ground elder had begun to take over the flowerbeds and she remembered that Ernie, the lad who helped in the garden, had been called up. She sighed, thinking that this war was beginning to affect every corner of life. She lifted the heavy brass knocker and let it fall.

"Hello, my dear," said the Vicar, taking both her hands. "How are you? And how's your mother?"

"We're both well, thank you Reverend Smythe. Mum's worried that Johnnie might be sent overseas."

"It's a trying time for all of us. Now if you'll just step into my study we can have our little chat and then we can join my wife and Mary. You will stay for tea, won't you?"

Margery sat on an upright chair facing the Vicar's desk. The fireplace was empty and the room was dark, shaded by a large chestnut tree. She knew it was usual for a young couple to see the Vicar together and she did miss Brian. She explained that his padre had agreed to go through everything with him, his duties and responsibilities, the service, the responses and so on. The Vicar listened, steepling his fingers together. He was a family friend and had known Margery since childhood; his daughter was her friend.

"So do you have a date in mind, my dear?"

"Not a precise date, only an approximate one. We're hoping for the 28th of May as his leave starts on the 24th but it depends; if the weather's bad, the boats can't cross the Channel so leave gets delayed. And then there's Hitler of course..." She looked out of the window and her voice trailed off, the words hanging in the air. The war was making everything uncertain.

"Yes, I understand. It's hard to be precise in these difficult times. If you're thinking of a wedding in May we need to get on with the Banns. They have to be read for three Sundays but then they're good for three months. Perhaps we should start them this week?"

"Yes, please. I think that would be a good idea." Posting the Banns made it seem very close and very grown up. Was it really less than a year since they had been playing tennis on the Vicarage lawn? No chance of that now; without Ernie, the court was overgrown.

"Brian's a good young man and I'm sure you'll be very happy together. We'll just talk through the implications of marriage as a Christian union. You will be promising to love, honour and obey Brian for the rest of your natural life."

Margery listened carefully as the Vicar went through his practiced routine. When he had finished they walked along the hall for tea. Margery took a thin slice of bread and some raspberry jam, still pippy she noted.

"It's such a shame you can't have the church bells for your wedding," said Mrs Smythe.

"They are only to be rung if the Germans land; that's the Bishop's orders. We wouldn't want the village to think there's an invasion, would we now?" said the Vicar.

"No, indeed," said Margery. Mary was eager to hear all the details, the clothes, the reception, the cake. Margery satisfied her curiousity. There was no doubt in her mind now; this was the right thing to do and she was excited.

"Just think, this time next month, you'll be a married woman, Margery."

England, 10th May 1940

Margery lay in bed and looked at the Bristol blue glass decanter and the glasses, a wedding present from Norah. She had put them in her room for safekeeping. Johnnie could be so clumsy when he larked around. Only ten more days now and Brian should be home; she hugged herself with excitement.

She could hear the radio as she walked down the hall. Bother, she thought, I don't want to hear about politics at breakfast; it makes me grumpy. She knew that Chamberlain had lost a vote of confidence, over that flop in Norway. Why did Mum have to listen to political shenanigans at breakfast time?

Nellie sat at the table smoking, and concentrating on the radio, her ear cocked like a robin. She wrung her hands together as Margery came in.

"Oh girl, it's bad news."

Margery raised her eyebrows; Nellie was ever the drama queen. Politics was boring, just old men quarrelling in that dreary House of Commons.

"Really Mum?" Margery waved her hand at the smoke. Nellie's next words were a bombshell.

"Hitler has sent his troops into Holland and Belgium.

The British Army is on the move."

"Oh no!" Margery sank into the nearest chair. She gasped for breath, her heart thudding, shocked to her very core. This was what she had dreaded. Brian had been in France for four months and nothing had happened – until now just before they were getting married. What dreadful timing! Her thoughts raced on.

"What about Brian?"

He would be on the move. Where would he be sent? What would he have to do? How would she know what was happening? She felt he was disappearing into the shadows, into a dark, unsafe corner where she couldn't reach him. Nellie shrugged.

"All leave is cancelled," she said. "That's all we know." Margery put her head on her arms and wept.

England, 2018

I grew up knowing about 'the wedding-that-didn't-happen'; it was always there, obscure and unexplained, something that grown-ups talked about while we children played on the floor or waited for a piece of cake. The story was the backdrop to my childhood. Whenever my parents' wedding was mentioned, my Uncle Johnnie would say:

"Was that the real wedding, Curly? Or the 'wedding-that-didn't-happen'?" Everyone would laugh, my parents included. Humour was the route to acceptance, after all.

I completely accepted it; I had no yardstick. I thought it was normal to have two events, a dress rehearsal and the real thing like we did with our school play. I never appreciated the pain, the disappointment, the frustration that lay beneath that family joke. I never realised... until I read the letters. They showed the story as it unfolded: the mounting excitement, the meticulous planning, the build-up and then... the let-down.

As I read the letters my chest tightened and I began to cry. I knew what was going to happen; but they didn't. They were passionate, eager, confident they would be married in a matter of days. Invitations were out, presents received, the church hall booked; it was going to happen. And then...

'What a bloody shame!' my father wrote. 'All our hopes dashed for the moment... I am terribly sick about it so near and yet so far.'

CHAPTER 10

France, 10th May 1940

Brian lay in his billet and heard Simon's regular breathing but sleep eluded Brian; ideas swirled around in his head chasing dreams away. Only ten days now until his leave began; how wonderful that would be. He remembered the little sapphire earrings he had asked his father to buy for Margery, a 21st birthday present to match her engagement ring. He thought of the journey across the Channel, wondered whether he would arrive in time to see Margery on that first evening. He thought about the service in West End Church and the honeymoon in Lyme Regis. His heart was rising with joy, building to a crescendo like the nightingales' song. Would they have nightingales in Dorset, he wondered?

This won't do; I'll wake Simon, he thought. Simon slept on his tummy, his arms above his head with one leg straight and one bent under him, the way he always slept. Brian turned over again, thumped up his pillow and fell into an uneasy sleep.

He woke at first light to the sound of rumbling lorries and tramping feet. Simon was at the open window, looking down into the cobbled street below.

"What is it? What's happening?" asked Brian, rubbing his eyes.

"The Glosters seem to be on the move. Something seems to have turned up. We'd better get ready and run along to HQ." They dressed and made their way along the street as the sun peeped out over Belgium, pink like the hint of a blister. It's always best to act sooner rather than later, thought Brian, with blisters and with Hitler. When they entered the Mess, they met the other officers, tense, excited, apprehensive, as they were.

"Now, gentlemen," said B-B. His leg was propped up on a stool, his colour was high. "I have to inform you that this morning the Germans have crossed their frontiers. They've invaded the Netherlands, Belgium and Luxembourg." A murmur ran around the room.

"This is what we're here for," said Major Heyworth.

"The Phoney War is over," said Elliot. "We'll have to crack on now."

Brian agreed but privately he wished that Hitler had waited a couple more weeks... until *after* his wedding.

"All leave is cancelled with immediate effect," said B-B, "that goes without saying."

We were so near, thought Brian, and now... so far. Margery will be disappointed but she'll understand. A couple of months' delay, that's all it is. We'll have our little scrap, stop the Germans and then, when the dust settles, leave will start again and *I'll* be top of the list. A summer wedding will be lovely.

"Our orders are to prepare to move," said B-B. "Men and equipment must be ready for action, everything packed up in kitbags. We don't know when we'll get the orders to go but it could be anytime."

A murmur of agreement ran through the officers. We've been here so long, thought Brian, it's come to feel familiar. We've felt the bitter cold of winter, seen the evenings lengthen and heard the first cuckoo. The town has absorbed us into its rhythms. But now, that's over; it's time to get on with the job.

"You must distribute the Field Service postcards. Each man must fill them in immediately." This struck home. Those pre-printed cards that were used in time of action as they did not need to be censored. They would tell friends and family that the men were well – but nothing else. What would Margery think when she received his card? No doubt she would read between the lines.

"I must remind you that nothing surplus to requirements can be taken. You know how it is; no doubt there will be all sorts of bits and pieces the lads have been hoarding, things that might come in handy but we must leave them behind. Then there's letters, photos and that sort of thing; they must go too. Every officer is responsible for his men. You must examine their kit and your inspections must be ruthless, gentlemen."

Brian thought of Margery's letters, those precious letters; he would send them home for safekeeping. The junior officers started muttering.

"We know this routine. We practised it with Ronnie," said Martin.

"B-B doesn't know that," said John.

"Quiet, please," said Simon.

The day passed in a flurry of work. Brian went around his company, checking the carriers, supporting his lieutenants and encouraging the men. All was well; their training had been thorough.

"That's quite a load you've got on there," said Brian to Private Jackson. "Good show. You've done a tremendous job with packing."

By evening, they were still there; and they didn't go the next day either. Other regiments were streaming through, moving forward to the front line, but not the Bucks. The frustration was tangible, a great cloud covering men and officers alike. Brian was asked the same question everywhere he went.

"When are *we* going to go, Sir? When will the buses come for *us*?" Jackson asked.

"At this rate it'll all be over before we get there," said Private Mills, watching trucks rumbling over the cobble stones. He was one of Elliot's lads from the printing works. Brian remembered him from the pre-war camps. He and Jackson were always together; they grew up in the same street and were both pretty handy with a football.

"They look good, don't they Sir," said Private Baker, one of the drivers. He was watching the trucks rumble by. "Bet old Adolf'll be sorry he took on us lot."

Brian thought that the BEF were putting on an impressive show of mechanised force; the French were still using horse-drawn transport, slow and cumbersome. Their army was not mobile; once they were in position they had to hold on, like a limpet.

The next day was Sunday and the battalion held their church parade, stepping out smartly in time with the band. This would be the last. They couldn't take the instruments with them; the bugles, the drums, the cornets would be left behind, stored in a cellar until the Bucks returned.

Brian took advantage of the temporary lull to write to Margery, commiserating with her disappointment over the wedding. He knew it would be the last letter he would write – for some time at least. He told her not to worry if she didn't get a letter for a while as he was not going to have much time for writing. She would chuckle over that deliberate understatement; she had always maintained it was a Dowling trait to play things down, in contrast to the Streets who specialised in melodrama. He wrote with care; he didn't want to alarm Margery but you never knew what might happen in battle and this letter might be his last, his legacy. He told her how much he loved her, what lovely memories he had of their days together and how much they both had to look forward to. She was his angel, his anchor, someone to whom he could reveal his innermost thoughts.

'Just keep hoping, darling,' he wrote.

The next day B-B called a company commanders' conference. He had news; they were to move forward on Tuesday 14th May, forward into Belgium, into action.

"That's more like it," said Martin as Brian relayed the orders to his lieutenants. "The lads can't wait to go." And go they did, moving along in good order, keeping regular distances between vehicles as they'd been trained to do.

Belgium, 16th May 1940

Two days later the battalion marched into Joli-Bois in Belgium on the edge of the Battlefield of Waterloo. They'd been marching all night along straight cobbled roads through flat featureless countryside, reaching the town as dawn broke. Brian looked round the cobbled square with its array of shops and cafés and put his kitbag down by the horse trough; he was ready for his breakfast.

"It's a shame those buses couldn't bring us all the way," said Bill, stirring sugar into his tea.

"I'm just thankful we've had so much marching practice." Brian took another slice of toast. "Eight miles is nothing to the lads now. B-B got that one right, at any rate."

"Those evacuees obstructed our progress," said John. "It was hard work weaving our way through that lot."

"Did you see that old man pushing his wife along in a wheelbarrow? She was clutching a budgie in a cage." The couple had struck a chord with Brian; they were about the same age as his parents. What would it be like if they had to evacuate their home? And how about Nellie and Margery? How would they fare if they had to leave Stone Cottage in a hurry?

"It must be hard if your home is in a battle zone," said Brian.

"Yes and these poor folks have been in the middle of every bloody conflict since God knows when. Did you notice the Waterloo monument on the little mound over there?"

"Yes, I did. Thank God for the Channel; it does a good job, stopping invaders."

"Yeah," said Bill, "but we'll stop this lot right here. That's the plan. We'll not let them anywhere near the Channel."

"I found the strategy meeting was a bit hazy yesterday," said John. "When B-B came back from Brigade HQ. He didn't seem sure about what we're meant to be doing."

"He gave so many options," said Bill. "We were to relieve the Moroccans, or to attack or to hang about for a bit. Do you think he'd got it muddled, Brian?"

"No." Brian stroked his moustache and chose his words carefully. "I'm sure it'll all come clear once we've unpacked."

He was concerned about B-B; he had seen him wincing

in pain and he wasn't as coherent as he used to be. He wished Ronnie was still in charge but he would keep his own counsel with his junior officers; they should trust their commander. By the time breakfast was eaten, new orders had come through from Brigade HQ and Heyworth relayed them to the company commanders.

"We've got to cover that anti-tank obstacle." Heyworth pointed down to a Mechano-like contraption in the valley below. "Get unpacked as quick as you can and get your men into position." Brian took the orders back to his company and told his platoon commanders. Everyone began to rush around and wild rumours spread, like wisps of mist in wind.

"They say Jerry's just over there," said Jackson, pointing across the valley. "Only a stone's throw away."

"I heard they are that way." Corporal Taylor pointed further to the left.

"Wherever they are they're too damned close for the likes of us," said Mills. "Damn well 'urry up and unload this bloody lot."

"Everybody down," said Brian. "Enemy planes!" The bullets whistled down, hitting the ground like hailstones. Brian hunkered down. His men were well hidden, but he felt they were vulnerable, stuck on the side of the hill in the open. Then, as quickly as they had come, the planes passed over. Brian muttered a prayer of thanks that no-one had been hit… this time.

Brian looked through his field glasses. He saw a stream, a road and a railway line ahead, but he couldn't see any Germans, only some French-Moroccan troops marching forward. His company had drilled, had trained, had waited to fight but now the enemy was elusive, playing hide-and-seek. B-B arrived by car to check progress – but he didn't get out. As he walked towards his colonel, Brian noticed that the man's face was florid and distressed.

"How's it going?" B-B's voice croaked a little.

"Everything is in order, Sir," Brian said. "These trenches only needed a little work and that's done now."

B-B was sweating, shaking and kept rubbing his leg.

"'e looks proper poorly, Sir," said Baker.

Later that morning Brian saw the Moroccan troops straggling back in disarray. They went through the lines and disappeared. Down by the anti-tank obstacle he could see horse-drawn transport, French of course; they too seemed to be retreating. But there was nothing else, no Germans to be seen.

There were clouds overhead, sending shadows scudding across the valley. The beech trees were breaking into leaf; they're always the last, thought Brian. Suddenly Brian saw other shadows; it was planes, bomber planes, flying low towards them. Brian felt like a mouse when the buzzard swoops.

"Duck!" called John. The shout rang out as bombs rained down. They shrieked and whistled before exploding like fireworks – Roman candles, Brian thought – only twice as loud.

"Bloody 'ell, they nearly got A company's HQ," said Jackson. The planes banked and turned, then flew back along the line.

"Keep down, lads," called Martin. Brian noticed a damp, sweet smell as shrapnel flew around, sharp and deadly and then there was a scream.

"Call the medics," said Brian. It was Private Hammond, one of his drivers. Brian went to see; but nothing could be done for him. It was a shock, their first casualty. He was a good lad, trustworthy and loyal; I'll have to write to his parents, thought Brian.

All that day, Brian was on the go, nerves taut, senses alert, and he'd been on the move most of the previous night too. He hadn't had a proper meal since breakfast and sleep seemed remote, unattainable. At last dusk softened the landscape and, as the long May day ended, the darkness increased Brian's disquiet. He heard rumours about enemy parachutists dropping behind their lines and he feared enemy soldiers lurking in the shadows. War's like an endurance test, he thought; you spend months waiting and doing nothing, then everything happens all at once and you must make life and death decisions when you're tired, hungry and thirsty – it's an uncomfortable business. Everyone was weary, on edge. Brian spoke briefly to Simon and learned that B-B was close to exhaustion.

"He's not been fully fit since he came back," Simon said. "And now, all this…" He gestured with his hands and shrugged. Just as dawn was breaking, Brian received the order to pack up, to withdraw his men and clear their positions by 8 o'clock.

"Withdraw?" said Martin when Brian gave him the orders. "We only just got here."

"I know, but those are our orders. I guess we're needed somewhere else."

They had been in Joli-Bois for just 24 hours; they had come under fire from enemy aircraft; they had watched the French go into action – and come back – but they had done no fighting. The men grumbled as they packed the equipment, evacuated the trenches and left Joli-Bois.

"I never even got a pop at Jerry," said Baker.

While they were packing up, B-B's condition deteriorated. The strain of the day – and the nights – was too much for him; he collapsed and the medics were called. He was too ill to go on and had to be evacuated.

"What a time to leave," said Brian. "I suppose our friend from Manchester will take over."

"Yes," said Simon. "Brian Heyworth's in charge; he's very competent. He's gone to report to Brigade HQ and to get orders. Elliot's to be second-in-command and he's overseeing our departure."

"That's good." That morning they left Joli-Bois on foot, marching back towards France on the long, cobbled road, lined with poplar trees.

19th May 1940

They marched by day, the sun pounding overhead, and they marched by night, with stars glimmering in the darkness. They trudged along, their feet pounding on the cobble stones, mile after mile after mile. The long May days were unseasonably hot. Brian's mouth felt dry and his stomach rumbled. How long was it since he had eaten a good meal? He couldn't remember. He felt sticky and uncomfortable under his battledress and there was a growth of stubble on his chin. He hadn't washed since he left his billet five days previously.

"Left... left... left... right... left."

Brian heard the chant as in a dream. He had had but six hours sleep since they set off but he must keep marching, keep in step. As they went along, he was asked the same question time and time again.

"Why are we withdrawing, Sir?"

"It's orders," he said, aware that didn't really answer the question. But *he* didn't know why; no-one did, not Heyworth, not Simon, not Elliot. It was bewildering. The battalion had been trained to fight, was ready to fight but they had done no fighting. It felt like a retreat, like they were on a moonlight flit; but they couldn't be... could they?

"Can't we have a go at 'em, Sir?" said Jackson. It was disconcerting and Brian felt something was wrong. All he could do was keep the men moving and encourage them as best he could.

"How's it going, Mills?" Brian asked.

"Not too bad, Sir. It'd be a darned sight easier if these damned Belgies would keep off the road."

"I know. There's no traffic control. You're doing well. Are you OK, Jackson?"

"Yes, Sir. Me and Mills are keeping each other company, telling jokes like."

"Good man," said Brian. "What about you, Baker? You're limping. Is there a problem?"

"I sprained me ankle, Sir. I slipped when we were digging them trenches at Waterloo."

"Right-ho, I'll see if I can squeeze you a place on the transport vehicle."

"Jammy bugger!" said Mills as Baker climbed onto the lorry.

The road was crowded with evacuees, fleeing the fighting as foxes flee the hounds. Brian noticed a mother with her children, each one with a small bundle. The youngest was clinging to a teddy bear. Brian remembered his nephew, little John, and his dogged attachment to a toy horse; what was it called? Paddaday, that was it. The evacuees clogged up the road, making it difficult to get into a good marching rhythm.

The women wore coats and headscarves, the men had jackets and caps. They walked, rode bicycles, pulled handcarts, and pushed prams, piled high with cooking pots, mattresses, chairs, whatever they could salvage from their homes. He saw an old man with a young woman, his daughter perhaps. They looked resigned, their heads down as they traipsed along in the same direction as the soldiers. So this is what war is like for civilians, Brian thought. A young woman pushed a bicycle with a bundle balanced on the saddle and Brian thought of Margery; the Belgian girl was about the same age but not nearly as pretty.

The road was so congested that the battalion came to a halt several times, total gridlock. The men were weary and, whenever they stopped, they fell asleep, on their feet sometimes. Major Heyworth came along the line, bustling with energy and orders like a bossy prefect.

"Come on, you lot. Look lively, there. You must keep them moving, Brian. We must be in a constant state of alert, you know." Brian did know; but how could they move when the road ahead was blocked? The conditions were punishing for men and officers alike.

After three days on the road the battalion arrived in Lesdain; it was to be a day of rest and recuperation and Brian felt glad. His men were still in good spirits but it had been hard for them, very hard. Rations arrived, and post. Brian sat by the roadside with his men and saw that they were well fed for the first time in a week. Then he turned to his letters. One from Margery and one from his father. He slit open Margery's letter, his heart leaping as he saw her writing again. It was full of wedding plans; it had been written before… before it all happened. He was reading when Simon strolled over, carrying a copy of *The Times*.

"Have you seen this, Brian old boy?" He held out the front page. Brian took it and read, the colour draining from his face.

"Crikey! So, that's it. The damned French!"

"Yes, it's a bit rich, isn't it?" Simon raised his eyebrows.

"For heavens' sake, we're meant to be helping *them* to defend *their* country and they're the ones who let the bloody Germans in. I can't believe it."

"It leaves us in a pretty tight spot, that's for sure," said Simon. "Heyworth is calling all the officers to an O group this evening to explain the situation."

"Right-ho. I'll tell my lieutenants."

When evening came all the officers assembled.

"Right, gentlemen," said Heyworth. "I'll try and bring together the information I've received from Brigade HQ and from the newspapers. It's all a bit confused but I'll do the best I can." This was the first time he had held an O group and the circumstances couldn't be worse. Poor chap, thought Brian, I expect he's nervous.

"We know that the Germans have broken through the French line to the south, near Sedan," said Heyworth. "That's the bad news. It means they've invaded France as well as Belgium."

"When did that happen?" asked Elliot. "Do we know?"

"It seems to have been early on. Their tanks went north of the Maginot Line, straight through the supposedly impenetrable Ardennes, met little resistance from the French so they got to Sedan in a matter of days – probably before we even reached Joli-Bois."

"*Blitzkrieg* again," said Martin. "Like they did in Poland. They don't hang about, these Huns."

"Do you know any more, Heyworth?" asked Rupert Barry, a tall officer with a handlebar moustache. He was in the Regular Army and had been seconded to the Bucks to take charge of C Company. "Can you understand what we're meant to be doing?"

"Yes, I think so." Heyworth stroked his chin. "You see, as the Jerries have broken through the French line, that gives them a clear run to Paris and to the Channel coast…"

"The Channel? Oh no!"

"What about the French?"

"What are they doing?"

"Haven't they any reserves?"

A barrage of questions came from all sides. Brian worried about Margery; if the Germans reached the Channel, what next? Heyworth held up his hand for silence.

"They have a clear run, I said, *unless we can get there first.*" He emphasised every word. "Our strategic priority is to protect our Army and stop the Germans reaching the coast and to do that, we need to reposition the line."

"That's a good way of putting it," said Elliot. "We're repositioning the line."

"We are to cover the flank as the British Army moves towards France. Those are our orders." He hesitated, his face tense as he drew his mouth into a hard line. "I must remind you that we need to be constantly watchful. The enemy are not far away. I am not happy with the battalion's state of alertness. Not happy all. The men are dropping off to sleep whenever we stop. I won't have that, do you understand?" He was almost shouting, his vowels flattening and marking him as an outsider. "You officers are *all* responsible. You must be firm and take steps to improve the position with your men." There was a bit of muttering amongst the junior officers; this was not the courteous approach they had come to expect in the battalion.

"We know you're all tired," said Elliot, his impeccable Oxford English in marked contrast to Heyworth's Mancunian accent. "And the men are too. But this is literally a matter of life and death; we do need to remain 120 per cent vigilant, gentlemen."

"I don't know any more," said Heyworth, turning away. "You can be sure though that I'll share information with you if anything else comes through."

21st May 1940

The battalion kept on the move, marching back towards France. From time to time they were strafed by enemy aircraft and took casualties. Sometimes they stopped to dig defences, to occupy trenches and to engage in a brief skirmish, but they were always moved on before any serious fighting took place. At Rumegies, they stopped again and took up a defensive position in the Gort Line, part of which they had helped to dig.

"Do you think we'll fight 'em 'ere, Sir?" asked Jackson.

"Maybe," said Brian. "For now, we need to cover that

stream. Tidy up these trenches so that we can hold the position."

"Yes, Sir." Jackson set to work strengthening their defences. But it was the same old story: in the early evening, the order came to withdraw and to march to Nomain. The roads were worse than before; in addition to the evacuees, French troops and horse-drawn transport were jostling for space, weaving here and there across the road and making orderly progress impossible. The French can't even march properly, Brian thought; frustration bubbled up, but he was too weary to be angry. In the chaos, the companies got separated from each other and Brian struggled to keep his men together.

"Look, Sir," said Jackson. "Is that Nomain over there?"

Brian consulted his map, looked across the fields and saw a small township, its tall church spire rising above the huddle of low buildings.

"Yes, I think it is. We'd do better across the fields,"

"Cross country route it is then." John led his platoon off the road into the fields. They reached Nomain at dawn; Elliot had gone ahead and had found billets for the men.

"Orders are to rest for the day," said Brian.

"Thank goodness," said John. "The lads in my platoon are getting pretty fed up with digging, taking up position, and moving on before the fighting starts."

"I know, it's hard on them."

In Nomain everyone went to sleep, the first time they'd all rested together since they left France, but by mid-morning, they were given different orders: to pack up and be ready to move. That was a blow as they had only had a few hours rest but the good news was their destination: Calais. Brian told his platoon commanders.

"Calais? Why that's nearly home."

"Just 20 miles across the Channel from Calais to Dover," said Bruce, always a ready source of information. Brian's spirits rose, and he began to think that perhaps it might not be so long before he saw Margery again. But they didn't go; they waited and waited… and waited. Food was scarce until foraging parties brought in pigs and chickens from surrounding farms and the smell of roasting meat filled the streets of the small township.

"This is more like it," said Mills, as food was passed round. Their departure was delayed again… and again as the day dragged on. Eventually, as darkness fell, the troop carriers arrived, and the men began to get on board.

"It's a bit of a squash, Sir," said Taylor.

"Yes, it looks like we could've done with a few more."

"Never mind, Sir," said Taylor. "We'll fit 'em all in somehow. Three to a seat now, lads. Don't be shy." The driver was standing by the bus, puzzling over his route card. He took off his cap and scratched his head.

"Are you ready, Baker?" Brian asked.

"Yes, Sir. But it says 'ere we're to go to Cassel."

"Put your specs on, lad," said Taylor, laughing. "We're off to Calais."

"That's not what's written 'ere." Baker squinted at the card. "'ave a look, Sir." Brian peered over his shoulder.

"It does say Cassel. Baker's quite right. There must have been a change of plan."

"Where's Cassel?" asked John.

"I'm not sure. I'll have to have a look at the map."

"It's a fortress town," said Bruce, who knew this part of France. "It's on a high hill with clear views all round. It's inland though – away from the coast." Brian's dreams of a wedding faded with the evening light.

As they proceeded through the darkness to Lille and Armentières, the battalion was at the back of the brigade convoy. Nothing between us and the Hun, thought Brian. He dozed fitfully, drifting in and out of sleep as the bus jerked along. He dreamed he was in a dodgem car with Margery beside him; he could feel himself pressing against her shoulder, her thigh. Johnnie was there too, and he kept bumping into them, jolting them. The air was heavy, fetid, smelling of stale cigarette smoke, and diesel.

He awoke with a start. Dawn was breaking as the vehicle came to a juddering halt. Brian rubbed the steam off the window and peered out; they had reached a crossroads. A military policeman stood in the road, his motorbike propped on the verge, and he was signalling for their vehicle to turn left, away from the main convoy.

"What's up here?" said Brian, rubbing his eyes.

"I think 'e's 'anding out new route cards, Sir." Baker wound down his window and took one. In the dim light, he peered at it.

"What does it say?"

"New destination, Sir." Baker passed the card to Brian and he read the word: Hazebrouck.

England, August 1992

"It's a twinning ceremony," my father said. He was standing by the bay window when I arrived to visit my

parents. They lived in an old cottage, looking across a quintessentially English village green, complete with duck pond and cricket match. He was watching a group of parish dignitaries gathered outside the village hall.

"We're twinning with a place in France," my father said, his eyes fixed on the ceremony, his mouth disdainful. The chair of the Parish Council was there with the chain of office around her neck and the flagpoles were flying the Union Jack and the French Tricoleur. We heard the band strike up 'God Save the Queen', followed by 'La Marseillaise'.

"They asked me to the dinner, as I used to be chairman of the Parish Council." Dad had never understood gender neutral language; for him, the business world was the world of men.

"But I refused."

"Why did you do that, Dad?"

"I don't trust the French. They're a load of cowards. When the Germans came, they just let them in. It was their country but they couldn't be bothered to fight." I knew he was talking about the war, harbouring grudges for events that happened before I was born. I liked France; to me it was a land of sun, good food, wine, holidays. I couldn't relate to his antagonism.

"But Dad that was all so long ago. They're our partners now in the European Union."

"Well, I don't know about that. They were our partners in the Entente Cordiale but it didn't stop them running away when the Germans came. Anyway I don't want to have dinner with them. I don't want to sit there and pretend to make polite conversation."

This was out of character; my father was a courteous man and a sociable one. My mother looked at me and shrugged her shoulders.

"Would you like a cup of tea?" she said as if tea could right the wrongs of years gone by. My father turned from the window, and his memories.

"I think we might have a little drink before dinner," he said. "What will you have, my dear?" The moment had passed, he was back in the present, the genial host once more.

CHAPTER 11

France, 24th May 1940

They trundled into Hazebrouck just as dawn was breaking. Brian jumped down and looked around the wide cobblestoned marketplace in the centre of the small town. The *Hotel de Ville* with its imposing pillars flanked one side of the square and they set up their camp kitchen at the foot of its steps. Brian could see little alleyways leading off in all directions, a veritable maze of streets going this way and that. They must usually bustle with activity, thought Brian, but not today. The town was eerily empty, the townspeople gone, like shadows.

Brian checked his men as they debussed and sent them to get breakfast. Simon walked across cobblestones and joined Brian as he finished eating.

"That hit the spot. I always say a proper breakfast sets you up for the day." Brian wiped his mouth and drained his mug of tea.

"Brian, old boy, Heyworth would like the company commanders to join him for a recce of the town. Did you know General Gort himself was here a day or two ago?"

"Was he indeed?" said Brian, picking up his steel helmet as he went off to join Heyworth's group. Captain Campbell, one of Gort's staff officers, came with them; his boots were shiny, his uniform pressed and his face glowing from soap and water. Brian had worn his battledress all night and all the previous day, and for several days prior to that. He was beginning to smell, like ripening cheese.

"Right," said Campbell. "I'll show you round the

defences and then it's over to you. It's been getting damned hot here, you know; we were shelled last week. It was one lone tank that lost its way."

Brian cast a glance at Rupert and Hugh and they raised their eyebrows. It sounded tame compared to their skirmishes on route.

The small town of Hazebrouck lay between the railway line and the canal, a network of narrow cobbled streets clustered around the main square. A patchwork of farms and fields stretched out beyond the town's perimeter and to the north lay Cassel where the rest of the brigade was deployed. There was a small wood overlooking the approach road from the south, the direction from which the enemy were expected to advance.

"That will be useful for hiding the artillery," said Rupert and Heyworth nodded.

"I'm assuming you will leave us maps, Campbell, so we can plan our strategy," said Heyworth. Campbell looked surprised.

"Well... you can have this one but I don't know whether there are any others."

"Really?" Heyworth's eyebrows shot up. "What about the other troops that are here? Can you tell me precisely how many men and arms will be coming under my command?"

Captain Campbell took off his cap and scratched his immaculately Brylcreemed head.

"I'm not sure, old boy, but I'll see what I can do to rustle up a list of some sort." Heyworth is asking all the right questions, thought Brian; he certainly knows his stuff but he's not getting much of an answer.

As they went around the town, they noted the existing defences, the expected line of the attack and the likely spots to set up artillery, company HQs and roadblocks. As they walked along the railway tracks towards the station they came across some GHQ staff making a bonfire. The acrid tang of smoke hit Brian's nostrils as scraps of blackened paper floated past, like feathers.

"They're burning the paperwork," said Campbell.

"It all seems too damned slapdash to me," Rupert Barry muttered to Brian. "That's Gort's strategic plans they're burning and Jerry could be here any time now."

Brian nodded. The defence of the town was just 'a spot of drill' from the way Campbell talked. I suppose it doesn't matter to him, though; he'll be off to join Gort but, for us, this battle is a matter of life or death. Once the tour was completed, Heyworth called all the officers together and outlined his strategy.

"Right, gentlemen, the overall position is this: the Germans have taken already Calais and are now to the west and south of us."

"No wonder we didn't go to Calais then," said Elliot. Dark images flooded into Brian's mind, the Germans crossing the Channel, Margery an evacuee with Nellie in a wheelbarrow, Doris and little John fleeing with Paddaday; they must stop them.

"The only way of saving the British Army is to get the troops to Dunkirk," Heyworth said. "The Navy can get us off from there." Alarm crept in like fog on the sea as Heyworth continued. "It'll take time to get the troops aboard the ships and back to Britain and time is in short supply, given the rate of the German advance – *Blitzkrieg* I think you called it, Martin. So, our job is to hold the Germans up, to stop them for as long as we can whilst our boys get things organised at Dunkirk. Hazebrouck will, of course, be a target for the Germans as Gort and GHQ was here. Our orders are to 'fight to the last man'." A ripple ran around the room as these words struck home. As he spoke, Brian's dreams of Margery, of their wedding, faded; they must stop the Germans, protect their loved ones from invasion; but… what would happen to the battalion, to the lads in his company, to him? Heyworth held up his hand for silence.

"We expect the advance to come along these roads from the south and the west," he said, pointing at the map. "Rupert and Hugh, I want C and D Companies on the outskirts covering these entry roads. Find yourselves some suitable spot for your HQ and then dig in along this line. Is that clear?" Rupert and Hugh nodded as Heyworth continued. "John, I want B Company to hold the railway line as far as the canal. The railway and the canal will deter the tanks' approach on the north and the east making your job easier. So that's the perimeters taken care of." Heyworth's got a good grasp of the lie of the land, thought Brian, and he's very efficient.

"Now for the centre of the town. A Company will be held in reserve in the *Institut St Jacques,* here." Heyworth tapped the map. "Brian, I want HQ Company to take over the defences within the town. I shall be setting up our HQ here in the *Fondation Warein,* just across the street from the *Institut St Jacques.* It'll be 'the Keep', the nerve centre of our operation. It's an orphanage run by nuns but they've all been evacuated so we have it to ourselves. It's the tallest building in town and we can get a view of the action all around from the top floor. We'll need good defences around that building, Brian. Now is that clear, gentlemen?" They all nodded.

"Are there any questions?"

"What about anti-tank artillery?" asked Rupert. "We're going to need some cover from big guns to deal with those tanks."

"The Surrey and Sussex Yeomanry and the Royal Artillery units are coming under my command and they will set up to cover the entry roads. Some of them will be in that little wood we saw this morning and we'll use the church tower as an observation post so that they can get the range. They'll give Jerry hell before he gets to you boys. How does that sound?"

"That's the ticket," said Rupert.

"Right, gentlemen. Off you go and get on with it. I am expecting Brigadier Somerset to come over the day after tomorrow to inspect our fortifications so let's make sure everything is in place by then."

France, 25th May 1940

It had been a busy day and in the evening Brian went into the nuns' garden to smoke. It's a good thing I've got a supply of Churchmans to help me relax. A blackbird was singing in a chestnut tree. These walls will help keep Jerry out, thought Brian, but they must have been built to keep the nuns in, secluded from the world. An old wisteria climbed the walls, its flowers throwing out their heady scent into the cool evening.

"How's it going, Brian?" Simon sat down beside him.

"Not too bad. The lads have put their backs into it and we're using some of those old French and Belgian tanks as roadblocks."

"Glad they were of some use. They didn't look as if they were up to much else."

"They've used farm carts, gates, anything they could scrounge to set up blocks at all the major intersections. It'll delay Jerry at least." Simon nodded as Brian continued. "It'll be hard for them to make much use of their tanks in the town centre; the streets are so narrow. That's in our favour."

"Reports suggest they're not far away." Simon had seen the incoming intelligence data. "They might be here tomorrow or the day after at the latest."

"Do you think we're really going to fight them this time, or will it be like all those other places? You know, dig in, organise the defences, a skirmish or two and then orders to move on."

"It's hard to tell, old boy, but my feeling, for what it's worth, is that this time it's the real thing." Brian pondered these words. "We'd better get some rest then while we can."

They went together to a bare dormitory where the narrow iron bedsteads lay in rows down the sides of the room. John and Martin were already resting, their kitbags open at the foot of their beds. The floor was bare boards, the windows without curtains, the walls unadorned except for a large wooden crucifix. It's a bleak life for an orphan, Brian thought.

The next morning, Brian washed and shaved ready for stand-to at 3am. It was the first time he'd put on clean clothes for over a week. He put Margery's letter in his battledress pocket to keep it with him. Then he set out to go around his company, checking the roadblocks and supporting his men as they got ready for action.

"Are we really going to fight this time, Sir?" Mills asked.

"Maybe," said Brian. "Enemy troops are certainly close by."

"Everybody down!" came a yell as enemy aircraft flew low, strafing and bombing as they went over the town but no-one was hurt… this time.

Apart from occasional air attacks, Saturday was quiet. Brian was glad to get two consecutive nights' rest, short as they were; the dormitory might be stark but at least it had beds and that was a relief after ten days on the road. Sunday morning was quiet but on Sunday evening they received a report of enemy tanks moving towards Hondeghem, a mile away – but they came no nearer. Was this going to be just another false alarm, Brian wondered? Will we be pulled out again? He didn't know; no-one did.

France, 27th May 1940

Brian rose before dawn on Monday morning; it was Margery's 21st birthday. Happy Birthday, darling, he thought. He ached to be with her, to see her face when she opened his present, to hold her in his arms, to kiss her. He looked out of the dormitory window and saw cloudy skies and misty rain. The weather had changed and his spirits plummeted with the temperature. He put Margery's letter into his kitbag in the dormitory; it was too precious to get wet. No sooner had he eaten breakfast than he heard the guns, a rumble like thunder and then the crack of the rifles. They sounded close, ominously close. He went around his platoons, having a word with his lieutenants and encouraging the men.

"Jerry seems to have got 'ere, Sir," said Roberts as the earth shook and the guns growled on the edge of town.

"Yes, C Company are in the thick of it." Brian made his way back to 'the Keep' and up the stone staircase. The huge crucifix served as a sombre reminder of mortality. On the top floor he found Elliot and Simon looking through their binoculars, like twitchers, except it wasn't birds they were watching.

"They're coming in along the Morbecque road… towards Rupert's positions," said Simon. "Our artillery has got the tanks in their sights." A series of explosions confirmed his words; dust rose in clouds and their ears rang as the ground shook and pieces of earth and metal flew upwards. Quite a spectacle, thought Brian, but unpleasant.

At lunchtime, Brian heard that Rupert's and Hugh's companies had both been in action, and that B Company had engaged the enemy along the railway line. Heyworth's strategy was working; the fighting was on the perimeter and the enemy hadn't penetrated the town itself. Brian and HQ Company were still in the wings, waiting for their turn at the action.

"Did you hear, Brian, that Brigade HQ sent a runner this morning with orders for us to move to Hondeghem?" said Simon, sitting down beside Brian in the cellars to eat his food.

"It's too late for that. Jerry is already here."

"We've had another report too, good news this time: the Navy are evacuating our troops from Dunkirk."

"That's grand. At least some of the boys are getting away."

"Dunkirk's the place to head for once we've done our job here," said Simon. "We might be able to slip away across the fields one night after dark, perhaps?"

"Mmm," said Brian, thinking of Margery. It wasn't far to Dunkirk, especially not cross country. Perhaps there might be a chance, just a chance… when their job was done here. As the afternoon wore on, the firing got heavier… and nearer. Elliot came over to Brian as he stood on the top floor watching the action.

"Rupert and Hugh seem to be copping it," said Brian.

"Yes," said Elliot. "Heyworth's sent up reinforcements from A Company. They're pretty hard pressed out there but it's difficult to make out exactly what's happening; the runners can't get through any longer. Brian, old boy, could you get your men to move the wounded into 'the Keep'?" Elliot was courteous as always. "The cellars seem the best place for our first aid post; they're big and strongly built, with an entrance each end."

"Right-ho." Brian set to work to organise his men.

By early evening Brian could hear shells falling in the centre of the town; he could see small fires blazing and he smelt smoke and gunpowder. The *Institut St Jacques* and 'the Keep' were both hit, but not badly damaged. The Germans were moving in, closer and closer to those roadblocks that Brian had inspected in the morning.

Casualties kept coming, some walking, some helped by comrades, some on stretchers. Each batch brought fresh information, a new bit of the puzzle. Men from the platoons on the perimeter came straggling in saying that the Germans had overrun their positions. Elliot and Heyworth tried to piece the jigsaw of information together; the Germans were creeping ever nearer to 'the Keep'. In the evening Jackson came in, with Mills resting on his shoulder.

"What's happened to you, boys?" Brian asked.

"They've reached our roadblock, Sir," said Jackson. "Mills caught a bullet so I lugged 'im back 'ere."

"Well done!" Brian realised that the Germans were nearer than he had thought. He reported the news to Heyworth and showed him where that roadblock had been.

As darkness fell, Heyworth called an O group in the schoolroom and Brian noticed that their numbers were gravely depleted; only Gort's staff officers and those from HQ Company faced Heyworth and Elliot. They sat at the wooden desks like abandoned orphans waiting for their lessons. The late evening light was slanting through the window, throwing a rosy glow onto the statue of the Virgin Mary standing in the corner. Several of the officers lit cigarettes.

"Gentlemen," Heyworth began, as usual. "The situation is serious. The Germans have come through C and D Companies and have penetrated our defences to the south. We have asked for reinforcements from Brigade HQ, but we don't know when they will arrive."

"It'll be hard for them to get here, won't it?" said Elliot. Heyworth narrowed his eyes and he frowned as he ignored this comment.

"We don't know yet what has happened to B Company and the battle along the railway line. They have certainly seen some heavy fighting; but the situation in that section is unclear. They might still be holding their position."

"I think we've done our job here," said Elliot, stroking his chin. "It's the duty of an officer to look after his men. We should get our men away now. I've known these lads since we were boys. That's always been the strength of the battalion." Heyworth scowled at Elliot; he hated to be reminded that he was an outsider.

Brian thought back to their classes in the autumn. *'Do the job and get as many of your men home as you can'*, that's what they'd been taught, back at Newbury. Perhaps Elliot had a point; they might be able to slip away in the darkness, reach Dunkirk and then, tomorrow or the next day, he'd be back to Margery. But Elliot was not in charge; Heyworth was.

"It's *our* duty to carry out *our orders*," said Heyworth, stabbing out his cigarette. But which orders, Brian thought? The last order was to move to Hondeghem, the one before that said to fight to the last man; the orders seemed to be out of kilter with the action.

"We've held them up," said Elliot. "We know the British Army has reached Dunkirk and the Navy is there, taking men back. We don't want to miss the boat, do we?" A ripple of laughter ran around the group.

"Our orders were to hold Hazebrouck *at all costs.*" Heyworth glared at Elliot. Brian noticed that Heyworth's speech was becoming more Mancunian, the consonants harder, the vowels flatter.

"And, *as I was saying,* we don't know what's happened to B Company." That's true, thought Brian, but why does he have to be so abrupt… so rude even?

"B Company is a crucial part of our strategy, that north-west section," Heyworth continued. That a good point, thought Brian; if they've fallen, then the Germans have surrounded us. "I need some recce patrols to go out and see if we can establish contact. Can you organise that, Brian?"

"Yes, of course," said Brian, looking at his lieutenants.

"Right, then. Let's see what the position is with B Company and then we can adjust our strategy in the light of the information. Thank you, gentlemen. That will be all." Turning on his heel Heyworth strode out of the schoolroom as Elliot put his head in his hands and sighed. Brian put out his cigarette, got up from his desk and went over to his lieutenants.

"David, Martin, can each of you take a couple of men and lead a recce patrol out towards B Company? David, you go towards their company HQ here," he said, pointing at the map. "And you, Martin, can you go through these small streets past the main square and along towards these positions. Report back to me when you've got news."

So, under cover of darkness, Martin and David picked their men and set out. Brian sat and smoked, cigarette after cigarette, as he waited for their return. He thought about Margery and her birthday; he hoped she was pleased with her earrings. He wished he could reread her letter but it was in his kitbag, where he'd left it this morning. Was that only this morning? It felt like a decade ago. It's a funny thing about time, he thought; some days slip by unnoticed while others you'll remember for the rest of your life. He had smoked half a dozen cigarettes before the men from Martin's platoon came back.

"Lieutenant Preston sent us back, Sir," said Hicks. "At

the corner. The main square's bloody crawling with Jerries. 'e said 'e'd 'ave a better chance of getting through alone."

"All right," said Brian. "Well done. You'd better go and get some rest now. Stand-to is at 3am; it's a short night." As the men went off, Brian lit another cigarette and his thoughts returned to Margery. Tomorrow – or was it today now? – was the day they had hoped to be married… if he'd gone on leave. He'd keep hoping their wedding wouldn't be long delayed; looking forward to it kept him going. It's like chocolate, he thought; you enjoy thinking about it almost as much as tasting it. He'd finished his packet of Churchmans and started another when David came back.

"We got through," he said, "but there was no-one there. Their HQ was deserted and there was no sign of anyone from B Company thereabouts."

"Right-ho," said Brian. "Well done! I'll let Heyworth know."

"Brian, you'd better tell him that there's Jerries everywhere. There's no chance of slipping out unnoticed. There's too damned many of them."

"Mmm. That bad, is it?" said Brian and David nodded. "You've done well, David. Go and get a bit of sleep now." Just as he was about to leave David turned back to Brian.

"What about Martin? Is he back?"

"No not yet. He sent his men back and went on alone. I'm still waiting for him to come in." David looked at Brian and nodded while Brian went on waiting – but Martin never came.

CHAPTER 12

England, May 1940

Margery walked across the dewy grass towards the stable, catching the scent of apple blossom on the soft morning air. Judy sniffed around the hedge, looking for rabbits or squirrels. Margery began her morning routine, putting Joey on his peg and chain, mucking out the stables, filling the hay nets and the water buckets. She heard the blackbird, pouring out his song of joy – but there was no joy in Margery's heart this morning. She took her grooming kit and began to brush Jack's silky coat, her muscles moving rhythmically until he gleamed like polished mahogany. He looked so well; you'd never know he was sixteen years old. He turned his big head and watched her trustingly as she worked. Her thoughts turned to Tinker, her first dog, and that dreadful day when he bit the postman. Her father had been adamant.

"We can't keep a dog that bites the tradesmen. Tinker must go." She had kicked and screamed and clawed at her father – but he took Tinker to the vet anyway, a one-way trip. It was his decision; Margery had only been a child. But she was a child no longer and this time it was her decision. She knew it had to be done but, in her heart, she was kicking and screaming just as before.

The war had really started now and it could go on for years, especially with that warmonger, Churchill, in charge. He had been Prime Minister less than a week but the outlook was bleak. '*Blood, toil, tears and sweat*' was what he was promising them. It had been one thing to wait and see about Jack while there was no fighting but it was different now. Johnnie was coming later today and he had made the arrangements. Her heart cried out in anguish.

"Time for breakfast," called Nellie from the kitchen doorway and Margery knew she must leave Jack behind. She heard the cuckoo calling from the woods, his notes echoing on the May morning as she went in for her boiled egg. Judy, her loyal friend, sat on her feet, under the table.

"How is he?" Nellie said.

"He's fit as a fiddle, but that's not the point, is it?" Margery spoke through gritted teeth as she attacked the top of her egg, sending pieces of shell into the yolk.

"No, I suppose not." Nellie shook her head as she looked at her daughter. She turned as the smell of burning toast seeped from the grill.

"I'm sorry, Mum," Margery said, in a tight little voice. "I didn't mean to snap at you. It's just… it's too much. I'm worried sick about Brian and now there's Jack."

"I know, girl."

Margery felt her mother touch her shoulder and tears pricked behind her eyes; she looked at the ceiling to stop them from falling.

"Anyway, Bert's been and he's brought something to cheer you up." Nellie drew two envelopes out of her apron pocket.

"They're from Brian." Margery sniffed and wiped her eyes on the back of her hand. Her fingers fumbled on the first envelope. She slit it, drew out the contents, glanced at the date, scanned the contents and put it aside with a sigh. Then she did the same with the second and groaned as she turned back to her egg.

"Bother! They were both posted two weeks ago before… you know… before it all happened. He was still looking forward to his leave and working out how to get petrol coupons for the honeymoon. He talks about nightingales, of all things." Margery rolled her eyes and sighed. These postal delays were infuriating. It was as if they were playing a funny game where the players were always out of sync. She and Nellie had spent the past week cancelling the wedding reception, retracting the invitations, and sending the presents back and then she gets this letter full of… things that weren't going to happen. She blinked and her bottom lip quivered.

"I know, girl, it's such a disappointment. By the way, I phoned Cousin Millie yesterday about the cake. She was so kind. She said that they can store it for you in their restaurant deep-freezer. If we take the icing off and send it back, she'll take care of that. And then, you can have it when he does get home and the wedding is on again. Now, that's a generous offer, isn't it?"

"Yes, Mum, it is," said Margery sniffing as she wiped her hand across her eyes. But would it ever be 'on again'? It felt flat with nothing to look forward to, like those bleak January days when Christmas was over.

"I'll do the washing up. You're a bit behindhand today."

"Thanks, Mum. I must change into my uniform ready for my shift." Margery left the table and made her way along the hallway to her bedroom.

She arrived at the hospital on time. Casualties had come in from Norway, that disastrous campaign which had brought Chamberlain down; they were really busy now. Margery welcomed the work as it took her mind off everything. The ward smelt of antiseptic and polish. Sister had put those new VADs on polishing and scrubbing, and Margery was glad that she was no longer the most junior nurse on the ward. She was trusted to look after the patients not the floors.

Margery made the bed for the young boy who had had his leg amputated; she washed the sergeant whose shoulder had been smashed by a bullet; she plumped up the pillows for the corporal with the shrapnel wound in his head. What sort of world was this, she wondered, where men were sent out to fight each other? She remembered how Johnnie had been punished at school for hitting another boy, yet now he was being trained to shoot and kill. The rules of behaviour had changed and, in this topsy-turvy world, fighting was commended – as long as your opponent was German.

"How are you feeling today, Corporal Jones?" she asked. He was sitting by his bed with his arm in a sling.

"Lots better now you're here, Nurse Street," he said winking at her. "Will you come down the pub with me this evening?"

"In your dreams! I'd get the sack." She'd had a difficult job yesterday evening getting the patients back into the ward before Night Sister came on duty. Those that could walk had gone down to the Nag's Head and, when Margery came for them, they were already merry.

"Have a drink with us, Nurse," Corporal Jones had said, his beery breath in her face.

"I can't. I'm on duty."

"Well, we won't tell, if you won't."

Margery had had a tricky job getting them back in time for Sister's round but she had managed it – just. She was in no mood for flirting today; she had a gnawing ache deep inside her.

The morning flashed past and soon it was lunchtime. Margery sniffed as she went into the canteen – boiled cabbage again, with cottage pie. The canteen rang with clattering cutlery, crashing crockery and cheerful chatter. She was glad to sit down, her feet ached; she hadn't had time to think of anything and that sad business would all be over by now. Tears pricked her eyes as she remembered. Peter came over carrying his tray.

"May I sit next to you, Margery?" he asked, smiling down at her. "What's up? You look rather wretched." Margery looked down at her pudding, spotted dick with custard. She decided to tell him about Jack: he was a good listener.

"Gosh! Poor you." He put his hand on hers. Margery flinched, uneasy at his touch; she liked him and he meant to be kind but it felt disloyal to Brian. She looked into his eyes and saw real concern; he was thoughtful, and a good doctor by all accounts, but he was not for her; she was promised to Brian.

"I must get crack on, back to work," she said, looking at her watch and getting up. Peter stood to let her pass and smiled at her, his eyes resting on her face.

That evening Margery sat with Johnnie under the shade of the pear tree drinking one of Nellie's endless cups of tea. The azaleas were in bloom, their potent scent filling the garden.

"It went very smoothly," he said. "I blew the hunting horn, Jack pricked up his ears... and that was it. He died looking for the hounds." Margery nodded.

"I'm glad it was quick," she said. She noticed the swallows, swooping, spinning, spiralling in the evening light. I feel I'm going round in circles too, she thought, worrying about Jack and Brian. She remembered the news that the Germans had cut through the Ardennes into France.

"Johnnie, you know this Ardennes business?" she said. "Why is it so important?" Geography was not her strong point but she knew it must be serious because Churchill had flown to France for talks with the French Prime Minister.

"It means the Jerries have by-passed our defences, Curly. They've come round behind our troops and now they can go anywhere… Paris, the coast, Britain even," said Johnnie.

"And what about Brian?" she said. "His last letter was written on 12th May just before he left… wherever he was for… wherever he's going." Margery hugged the letter to herself like treasure. It was a very special letter, particularly tender and loving; he had called her 'his anchor', 'his angel', and had said how much he cherished his memories of her. It was the sort of letter soldiers wrote before… But she mustn't think like that.

"Oh, he'll be busy, very busy, trying to stop the Germans cutting them off. Poor old Bri, marching along in Belgium in this heat. What a way to see the world, eh?" Johnnie finished his tea and got up to go. "Chin up, old girl. Keep hoping." He turned back, putting his hand on Margery's shoulder as he said, "…and keep praying."

Margery looked up at him sharply. Did he know more than he was letting on? He was a soldier after all.

England, 27th May 1940

On her birthday morning Margery lay in bed thinking of Brian. The weather had broken and her bedroom felt stuffy, heavy with thunder, and foreboding. He had planned to be with her for her birthday, home on leave. Hitler's onslaught was a watershed cutting her world in two; before the attack had been Brian's leave, Jack and the wedding but after the attack was emptiness. Perhaps though, Brian might be in touch? A telegram or a letter? He knew it was significant, the day she came of age and she kept hoping for something. Nellie had planned a tea party for this afternoon but the guests seemed singularly ill-assorted – her family, Fleda, Norah and Brian's parents. Margery sighed. She knew she must pretend to enjoy it; Nellie was trying so hard to cheer her up. But there were some things that were too serious to be cured by tea and cake whatever Nellie thought. She sighed again as she got out of bed.

"Happy Birthday," said Nellie as Margery came into the kitchen for breakfast. She noticed presents by her plate and then Bert knocked on the open door.

"I think someone's got a birthday today," he said, handing Margery a bundle of cards. "Happy Birthday, Miss."

"Thank you, Bert." Margery's fingers twitched at the envelopes; she wanted to see whether the one she longed for was there but she couldn't look while Bert was there; that would be impolite.

"Will you have a cup of tea, Bert?" Nellie asked.

"Oh, I'd love one, but I think I'd better bang on. It looks like we're in for a storm." He turned to leave and Margery flicked through the pile of cards, hearing the first rumble of thunder in the distance. No, it wasn't there; no card from Brian. She sat down, feeling like a punctured tyre.

"He'd wish you Happy Birthday, if he were able to, old girl," Johnnie said. "You know he would. Good old Bri would never miss your 21st if he could help it."

"I suppose so." Margery still hoped for a message, a miracle. The thunder crashed again, nearer now and the rain began to pour down.

By mid-afternoon the guests assembled in the sitting room for the party. Fleda walked round with a big umbrella and flopped down on the sofa beside the empty fireplace. Johnnie had taken the car to fetch Norah and Amy and Frank Dowling. As she came in, Amy handed Margery a small package.

"Some of my oatmeal biscuits," she said, her tight little smile barely creasing her lips. "I'll show you how to make them one day. They're Brian's favourite." Margery knew he preferred chocolate biscuits – but they never had those in the Dowling household. Norah gave Margery a bottle of sherry to go in the Bristol Blue glass decanter that had been her wedding gift.

"Oh, that's topping," said Margery. "Let's all have a glass, to celebrate."

Johnnie fetched the glasses, poured the sherry and handed it around.

"Not for me, thank you." Amy pursed her lips and shook her head. "I never indulge." Johnnie offered the tray to Fleda, Nellie and then to Frank.

"Just a small glass perhaps," said Frank. "To drink Margery's good health."

Fleda had found a silk nightdress, a rarity nowadays, and she presented it to Margery, still in its paper bag from the shop. Margery peeped in and pulled it out. The silk rippled under her fingers like running water.

"You'll look the bee's knees," said Nellie.

"I was cock-a-hoop when I found it. I thought it'd be just right for the honeymoon," Fleda said, winking.

"Brian will get a real treat when he sees you in that," Johnnie said, but Amy sniffed. She disapproves, Margery thought; she's so stiff and scratchy like a starched collar. Frank was different altogether, kind, courteous and good. He drew a small package, wrapped in tissue paper, from his pocket and passed it to Margery.

"I hope it's all right, my dear," he said, his eyes twinkling behind his glasses. "I tried to follow my orders as best I could." What does he mean, Margery thought? She unwrapped the package carefully so that the paper could be re-used; there was a war on after all. She opened the little box and, nestling inside on a velvet bed, were a pair of earrings. The diamonds glittered offsetting the sapphires as she lifted them from their nest and held them up to her ears.

"Oh thank you." Her eyes shone with joy. "Are they from Brian? They match my engagement ring." She thought back to the day they had bought the ring; how happy they had been, so carefree, so joyful, so young.

"Yes, my dear," Frank said, bending to kiss her cheek. "He gave me precise instructions and I hope I've discharged the commission. He hoped to be here himself, of course." Brian had been so thoughtful; he hadn't forgotten her birthday – but he wasn't there, he wasn't coming. The earrings underlined his absence. Margery sank onto the sofa, the tears running down her face.

"Oh Margery," said Norah, putting her arm around her friend. She sat down on the arm of her chair and produced her handkerchief.

"Let's leave these girls for a minute," said Nellie. "You can all help me to set out the tea." Amy pursed her lips and sniffed; Margery knew she disapproved of this show of emotion but, all the same, she went with Nellie to the kitchen and the others followed.

"Come now, blow your nose," said Norah. Margery gulped and wiped her face but the tears continued to flow. "They're lovely earrings and a perfect match for your ring. Brian's very considerate."

"Yes," said Margery, sniffing. "But it's so hard, him being away when we'd planned the wedding and everything. I feel so wretched."

"I know you do." Norah rubbed Margery's back. "You've got a lot to put up with just now – no wedding, no Brian and no Jack. I never realised this war would upset our lives so much. I just hadn't the foggiest."

"Nor did I." Margery hiccoughed as the sobs rose again. "Last year all I thought about was parties but now everything's smashed to smithereens; there's so much to accept, so many choices to make and such a lot to worry about. I don't think I like being grown-up." Norah smiled at her friend. "Then there's Brian's parents; I feel so raw with these constant reminders that he isn't here."

Norah nodded. There was a brief silence while the two girls were lost in thought. Then Norah got up and walked past the fireplace and over to the French windows.

"This weather doesn't help, does it?" Outside, the thunder rumbled and a flash of lightening lit the room. She turned back to Margery.

"Do you feel you can put a brave face on it and join the others? You are the Birthday Girl after all." Margery blew her nose and lifted her chin.

"I'm ready," she said.

Later that evening, when Johnnie had driven their guests home, he found Margery alone in the sitting room turning the earrings over in her hands. He sat beside her and put his hand on her arm.

"Curly, I popped into the pub on the way home and met a chum. He told me some news." She looked up at him, wondering what this might be about. "The Navy is bringing our soldiers home, evacuating them from Dunkirk. It's Churchill's scheme and it started today. There's not many yet but, with luck, they'll all be back within the week."

Margery's heart leaped and her eyes shone. 'All be back within the week' Johnnie had said; surely that would include Brian? Just at that moment the evening sun broke through the dark clouds for the first time that day.

CHAPTER 13

France, 28th May 1940

At first light, Elliot crossed the cobbled street with Charles, the Quartermaster, to the *Institut St Jacques*; they were going to scrounge food and ammunition, both of which were running short in 'the Keep'. They found spam, dried egg powder, and biscuits.

"That'll do," said Elliot. When they brought the stores back to 'the Keep', the cooks served a hot meal in the cellars, beside the first aid post, the tang of blood and disinfectant mingling with the sulphur from the egg powder.

"I'm glad of that," said Brian taking his plate of food. The scrambled egg smelled tainted and the spam looked pink – like bare flesh on a beach, Brian thought. But he was hungry after his night-long vigil. He ate his meal and drank his tea, wondering what the nuns used the cellars for; they were cavernous, gloomy, tomblike. He shivered as he made his way amongst the wounded to find Mills.

"How are you feeling this morning?"

"Not so bad, Sir." Mills smiled weakly. He looked ashen in the dim light. "I was lucky Jackson brought me in before I lost more blood. It's only a flesh wound." There were about two dozen wounded men in the cellars, from all companies. Yesterday's fighting has taken its toll, Brian thought, and these are the lucky ones. He didn't want to think about the others – those like Martin who were simply missing.

He went outside to supervise the unloading of the ammunition truck; Elliot had done a good job and he helped his men to lift the cases and carry them into 'the Keep'. No doubt we're going to need this lot before the day's out, he thought. Suddenly, there was a rumble, a whistling and a bang; one of the ammo trucks had been hit.

"Run!" Brian shouted and they all took cover. The truck was still half-full and a series of explosions began; a cacophony of sound and flames. Other vehicles caught alight, and the smell of burning rubber mixed with the cordite. The air around 'the Keep' was filled with black smoke and, as it drifted aside, they saw a party of German infantrymen walking towards them, guns at the ready. The smoke had provided cover for the enemy to scale the wall and enter the garden.

"Tommy, give up. You are surrounded," they called in accented English.

"Open fire!" Brian yelled. Rifle shots rang out and the Germans took cover and withdrew. One man remained, his body lying in the garden.

Later that morning 'the Keep' came under heavy fire from tanks, one of which came along the road to the front of the building. The air crackled with rifle fire, echoing around the narrow street, and the ground shook as shells exploded, sending metal, earth and men flying upwards. HQ Company drove that tank back but soon more appeared, a never-ending stream. Snipers and machine gun fire compounded the attack and HQ Company took more casualties. Brian helped to carry the wounded down to the cellars. They're filling up down here, he thought.

In the early afternoon Brian stood at a first floor window, his rifle trained on the end of the street; German motorbike riders were trying to cross the gap between the buildings. He watched as a motorbike edged around the corner; I must wait till he's clearly in my sights, he thought. Then he aimed, fired and saw the bike skid as its rider fell motionless, his helmet spinning in the gutter. The adrenaline rushed and Brian rejoiced that he had hit his target. Then he remembered that 'the target' had been a man, someone's son, someone's sweetheart.

The Germans were everywhere and seemed to have inexhaustible supplies of ammunition, guns and tanks; they just kept coming, like stormy waves on a beach. The men in 'the Keep' were hard-pressed, but Brian knew no help could come. 'The Keep' no longer felt like a fortress; it reminded Brian of those castles of cards, the ones that would collapse in an instant.

In mid-afternoon there was a lull in the fighting. No motorbikes, no tanks, no shells and the town fell eerily quiet. The officers gathered in the school room and Elliot came round with a box of cigars.

"I don't want these to fall to the Hun. Would you care to have one, Brian?"

"I love a good cigar." Brian rolled it between his fingers and sniffed. "Thank you very much." As Elliot went around distributing his cigars to everyone, officers and men alike, the air became redolent with the rich leafy smoke.

"Lovely," said Simon, inhaling deeply. "It reminds me of a good dinner and a bottle of port."

"It reminds me of Christmas. I proposed to Margery on Boxing Day."

"Good memories, eh Brian? I wonder where we'll all be next Christmas?" They smiled at each other, savouring the moment and their cigars. The dust, the smoke, the destruction of the buildings on either side of them were dispelled as they reminisced. Then Heyworth began to talk.

"How much ammo have we got left, Brian?"

"Just a couple of cases," Brian said. "We've been using it pretty heavily all morning."

"Redistribute what we've got. Some of those men GHQ left behind hardly know how to hold a gun, let alone fire one!"

"All right, I'll see to it."

"I'm going over the road to see if I can scrounge some more," said Heyworth. "Elliot, you're in charge here till I get back."

"Right-ho. Watch out for those snipers on the roof across the street."

Major Heyworth left the building through the cellar door while Brian went through 'the Keep' redistributing the precious little ammunition that was left. He was on the second floor when tanks came rolling down the street, firing shells into all the buildings; the lull was over. The top floor of 'the Keep' was hit and began to burn. The blaze was fierce and the ceiling of the second floor began to collapse.

"Everybody out!" Brian yelled. He choked with the dust and the fumes. A stream of men rushed past him through the smoke, their battledresses covered in brick powder. Brian looked around the room; one man was huddled by the window. Forbes lay bleeding, trapped by a fallen beam.

"You go, Sir. Leave me."

"Come on," said Brian, lifting the beam and hitching Forbes over his shoulders. He carried him down the stone staircase to the cellars to join the queue of wounded waiting for attention. There's more than twice as many casualties as there were at breakfast, thought Brian, but no wonder. Just then there was another crash: a direct hit on the building. Cracks appeared in the ceiling of the cellars and brick dust trickled down like powdery snow. Clouds of smoke were billowing down the staircase; the crackle of flames added to the snap of rifle fire and the boom of shells. The noises echoed round the hollow, dimly lit space. Everybody came down to the cellars. This building is not going to stand much more, Brian thought. Elliot called the officers together in the cellars.

"We'll have to get out and hole up somewhere till nightfall," he said.

"Then get to Dunkirk," said Simon.

"Yes, if we can. Best to go out the east door. We can hide in those houses along the street, or else in the nuns' garden."

"Their line of advance is from the east. How about the west door and over the wall?"

"The wounded can't scale that wall," said Elliot. "Simon, you could lead a small group that way if you want."

"Right-ho," said Simon. "Do you want to come with me, Brian?"

Brian looked at his friend and looked at his men, those that were left. He knew he couldn't leave them.

"No, I'll stay with my men."

"Right then, old chap, I'll see you in Dunkirk." Simon opened the door and left the building with a handful of men.

"Good luck, Simon." Brian turned to go with Elliot, leaving by the east door and running to the low houses bordering the street. The tanks were right outside and the

Germans lobbed hand grenades through the windows. They were sitting ducks; they had to get out.

"Into the garden," said Elliot and Brian led his men into the shrubs. The scent of lilac mingled with the smell of smoke and dust. As Brian crouched in the walled garden, there was a roar as the upper floors of the *Fondation Warein* came crashing down. I hope the cellars are still holding, thought Brian. Then the Germans moved into the garden. They looked at the body of the infantryman still lying where it had fallen that morning; one of them poked him with his toe.

"The game's up," said Elliot. "We've no ammo, no shelter and we've been seen." He threw down his rifle and came out with his hands in the air, surrendering his party to the Germans.

"For you, Tommy, the war is over." The infantryman repeated the catchphrase in heavily accented English. "Line up by that wall." The German soldiers stepped back and raised their sub-machine guns. Brian stood beside Elliot. I must set an example, he thought, as he tried to control his legs which seemed to be shaking. This must be revenge for the men we've killed. Suddenly Elliot saw a high ranking German officer. He knew the Germans respected rank and he called out.

"*Herr Oberst.*" The officer looked their way. *"Ich bin Major and er ist Hauptmann."* The German officer came over and exchanged some rapid words with their captors.

England, 2016

I was about six when first I heard the story of Dunkirk – the one you've all heard about the little ships taking the soldiers off the beaches and how it was 'our finest hour'. Sally, the class braggart, told us her father was a hero; he was in the Royal Navy and he had saved the British Army. I listened to her cocksure confidence and envisaged her father, single-handed, at his task. I desperately wanted to compete. I knew my father had been in France in 1940.

"Were you at Dunkirk, Dad?" I asked the next morning as he was dressing.

"Not quite," he said, shaking his head as he sat on the bed. "We were going in a convoy towards Dunkirk and my battalion was at the back... and when we came to a crossroads..." He always started the story at that crossroads, as if for him it were the Rubicon.

"When we came to a crossroads the rest of the troops went straight on..." His voice was fading, his eyes no longer focusing on me. He paused, with his sock in his hand, seeing men I'd never known.

"The rest of the troops went straight on but we didn't... we went left..." He withdrew from me as he drowned in his story, in his past.

"We met the Germans... and there was a battle..." He was totally submerged now, the words rising slowly like bubbles.

"And when the building caught fire... I ran out into the garden... and I was captured." I sensed his pain, throbbing like a heartbeat.

"Couldn't you escape?" I persisted, desperate for at least one heroic act to tell Sally.

"They had guns," he said, "and we were out of ammunition." I asked no more. His story sounded as if he had gone the wrong way, got lost and blundered into the Germans.

I'd better keep quiet at school; he wasn't a hero, not at all.

A lifetime later, I realised there were countless stories of Dunkirk, told to different audiences for different reasons. There was Churchill's story of the little ships and 'our finest hour', its purpose to boost public morale in the face of 'a colossal military disaster'. There was Sally's story, her attempt to gain pre-eminence amongst her classmates. And there was my father's story; but his was like a tree in winter, its stark, bare structure merely hinting at its summer grandeur. It reflected pain, pride, and shame, jumbled together like conflicting flavours in a highly spiced dish. When he first told it to me, I was too young to unravel the complexities of this intricate web.

It was sixty years before I explored further. I googled his battalion's history and found an account of the Battle of Hazebrouck 1940. My heart leapt, my stomach churned and my eyes filled with tears. This was it; I had found it, the Bucks Battalion's story – and my father's. The details were the same: the crossroads, the battle, the burning building, the surrender in the garden. But the framework was different.

The crossroads was indeed a Rubicon but he hadn't got lost; he was obeying orders, terrible orders. They had fought well but it was like twigs trying to hold back a river. They had delayed the Germans for two days, long enough for the Dunkirk evacuation to get started. They stopped the Germans encircling the British Army, cutting them off from the coast and bringing the war to a prompt conclusion. He was captured to enable others to get back to Britain and fight on. But he never referred to it as his moment of glory. He downplayed his part in the battle, even though he was 'Mentioned in Dispatches'. He was a hero – but he never told me.

CHAPTER 14

England, June 1940

"Nurse Street, you are to change the dressings, tidy the beds and straighten the pillows," said Sister as Margery stood in front of her desk with her hands behind her back. Fanny Dobson – they called all the Sisters 'Fanny' – spoke only of equipment not of people; that's typical, she thought.

"And no gossiping, mind, or we'll never get done."

"Yes Sister," said Margery, keeping her eyes down. This was the way every shift started. She buzzed along the row of iron beds, never still for a moment. The ward was very busy and they had put in extra beds as the casualties flooded in from Dunkirk. The nurses' shoes clicked, the doors clattered and the tea trolley clanged. Margery welcomed the bustle; it kept her fears at bay.

"I've come to change your dressing, Private Woods. What happened to you?"

"I caught a bit of shrapnel on the beaches, Nurse."

"Are you just back from Dunkirk?"

"Yes. I'm one of the lucky ones. Those that couldn't walk 'ad to be left behind." Margery tried to concentrate on the bandage. Brian had not returned. Might he be one of those they'd left behind?

"Oh dear! I didn't know it was as bad as that. Do you know what happened to the Bucks Battalion?" She asked everyone the same question.

"The Bucks, Nurse? No. Why do you ask?"

"My fiancé is with them. We're going to get married on his first leave."

"Lucky chap."

Margery hoped he was lucky, hoped he'd come home. She finished the dressing and moved along to the next bed.

"How are you today, Private Robbins? Feeling any better?"

"Lots better for seeing you, Nurse."

Margery smiled and shook her head as he winked at her; she was used to their banter. She changed his pillowslip, turning the open end away from the door; it looked tidier that way. In the next bed was a new patient, a young man with his arm in a sling. He was new on the ward.

"Hello there. What's happened to you?"

"I got in the way of a bullet, worse luck. I was one of the last, you see."

"Well, I'll just tidy you up, ready for Doctor. Do you have any news of the Bucks Battalion?"

"The Bucks? That lot were sent over Cassel way, weren't they?" He turned to Private Robbins, who was shaking his head and putting his finger to his lips. The young soldier scratched his head with his good hand.

"I dunno, maybe that was some other lot; it was a right old muddle out there." Margery sighed; no-one seemed to know about the Bucks – or if they did, they wouldn't say. An invisible barrier had descended, cutting her off from all news of Brian. She took the dirty linen into the sluice room, where the smell of bedpans defied the disinfectant. Peter followed her in and shut the door.

"Margery, I couldn't help hearing what you said to that patient in Bed 9. Is there still no news of Brian?"

Margery shook her head; she couldn't trust her voice. She felt so raw.

"It was an awful mess out there, you know. We're still getting people coming in." Peter came nearer and looked into her face. She knew he meant to be kind but she wanted to hide away like a wounded animal.

"Not many now," she said, looking away from him and sniffing. "The boats have stopped coming back. Almost everyone else has heard. Mrs Batt next door, her Bob rang home and said he was safe. Then my friend Mary heard that her brother is in hospital in Kent. Mrs Cheeseman in our village, her two boys are back and home on leave. But no-one seems to know about Brian and the Bucks."

Tears were running down Margery's face and her voice was shaking. Peter's solid presence was so reassuring that Margery buried her face in his chest and wept.

Margery's shift changed and she found it hard to sleep when she was on night duty. The daylight peeped through the curtains and thoughts of Brian swirled around her head. She ached for news, any sort of news; it was weeks now since she'd heard from him and not knowing what had happened was wearing her down. When she looked in the mirror, her skin looked stretched and she had dark circles round her eyes, like those clowns she'd seen at the circus with Brian. Her face was hollow, her uniform slack and her belt needed extra holes.

She lay in bed staring at the picture of *The Light of the World* on her wall; the picture seemed gloomy, at one with her mood. She could hear noises from the kitchen; Nellie was preparing for the party, the one they were hosting for the 'Dunkirk Boys' from the hospital. She wouldn't get any more sleep now; her clock told her that she'd had five hours and that would have to do. If it was a quiet night, she might be able to doze a bit on the ward. She opened her wardrobe and took her light cotton frock off its hanger, put it on and buckled the belt around her waist. Then she padded down the hall towards the kitchen. The door was open and she could hear Nellie's voice as snatches of conversation drifted towards her unbidden.

"...nothing. We fear the worst of course..."

She wished Nellie wouldn't talk about it, about Brian, about her. It didn't help and nobody knew anything yet, not for certain. She cleared her throat before she went into the kitchen. Kathleen Miles was standing by the back door talking to Nellie.

"Hello, Mrs Miles. Hello, Mum."

"Hello, girl. You awake then?" Nellie stood at the table beating cakes and smoking. Her ash dangled dangerously near to the mixing bowl. Margery knew that the sugar for the cakes was the rations they'd saved for her wedding. She felt a traitor, as if using the sugar meant she'd given up on Brian. Those cakes would be spoiled if Nellie didn't pay attention; her cigarette ash wobbled, teetered, was about to land in the cake mixture until Nellie gave a practised flick and it fell clear; she was a seasoned performer.

"Well, I must get out of your way," said Kathleen. "I only came over to drop in this Dundee cake, Margery. My aunt sent it from Canada. I thought it'd be just the ticket for those brave boys."

"Thank you Mrs Miles. That's very kind. It'll be a real treat. What can I do to help, Mum?"

"Perhaps you could make a start on the sandwiches, girl?"

Margery went to the table and started to cut the bread. Judy lurked around hoping for a crust but she was out of luck as Margery left them on. Alf from next door had given them a pot of honey, their hens laid well and they had a pot of meat paste. The Dunkirk boys would be well provided for.

Fleda arrived with her usual bustle.

"It's like an oven out there. They'll have to sit in the shade or we'll have our Dunkirk boys dying of heatstroke. That won't do after all they've been through. What time are they coming?"

"About 4.15. Matron said that would work well so they can get back before the evening rounds," said Margery.

"Oh Fleda, could you make a start on the washing up?" asked Nellie. "The dirty dishes are getting a bit crowded on the draining board."

"Well, I don't get much practice but I'll have a go. Anything to help with the Dunkirk Jamboree." Fleda rolled up her sleeves and turned on the taps. Peter knocked gently on the back door and poked his head into the busy little kitchen.

"Hello there. I thought I'd come a bit early to give you folks a hand. It's so good of you to host this party, Mrs Street. The patients were cock-a-hoop when they heard about it. It's given them something to look forward to."

"It's only a little thing. Those poor boys, they have been through the thick of it and we had all the food, of course, ready for the other party." Nellie nodded her head in Margery's direction and Peter's eyes followed her gaze. "I hope it bucks them up, the poor boys."

"I'm sure it'll help us all to keep our chins up. Now what can I do to help?"

"Perhaps you and Margery could take some chairs outside?" Margery left the sandwiches and helped Peter to carry the dining room chairs into the garden; they set as many as possible in the shade of the old pear tree and the rest were clustered around the lawn. The herbaceous beds were at their best, the lady's mantle spilling over the hardy geraniums in a riotous blend of pastel shades while the willow tree cascaded its emerald curtain over the end of the lawn.

"What a pretty garden. It's so green, here," said Peter. "We get very little rain in South Africa and our gardens never look like this."

"I'd love to hear about it one day," said Margery. "Brian talks of going to South Africa, after the war." She brought him into the conversation like a shield. She felt shy with Peter in her own home; it was more intimate, more personal than at the hospital. When the guests started to arrive, Nellie directed them into the garden.

"Mrs Street," said Private Robbins. "Would you mind if I took my jacket off? I'm fair cooking."

"Go ahead, all of you. Make yourselves comfortable." The boys sat around in their braces and shirt sleeves, balancing plates on their knees. Margery heard snatches of conversation as she moved from group to group, refilling their teacups, while Judy ambled at her heels, hoping for titbits.

"Bit different from them beaches, ain't it?"

"I'll say. Three weeks ago I thought I'd never see a garden again."

"I thank me lucky stars I got back."

"It was the noise that got me. A hell of a din. Makes a change to hear a bit of birdsong, don't it?"

"We're so proud of you, our brave boys." Nellie offered sandwiches and cake to her guests.

"I don't know about brave, Mrs Street. I was dead scared, I don't mind telling you," said Private Woods.

"You're our heroes from Dunkirk," Nellie said, moving on to another group.

"I don't feel much like an 'ero, Mrs Street. When them boats came, I was that desperate, I just scrambled aboard."

As she went to refill her teapot, Margery thought how chaotic it sounded. These lads had been lucky but had Brian been one of the unlucky ones? He seemed to have gone to France and then disappeared. 'Lost in France' they said. It sounded like he was wandering around looking for the way home; it was her personal nightmare while the nation worried about a German invasion. They'd reached the Channel Islands and it was such a short step to the south coast of England. Last year Margery and Brian had gone swimming on the beach at Dover but now that same beach was mined and guarded against enemy invaders. She turned from these gloomy thoughts to refill the teacups. Perhaps Nellie was right to focus on tea and cake; worrying didn't help.

England, August 1940

Margery took a clean nightie out of her drawer and gazed at Brian's letters. It was over two months since she had heard from him and she ached to know he was safe, to hear what had happened but Bert brought no more letters. As she was about to undress, she heard the church bells sounding the alarm and Nellie poked her head round the door.

"Quick girl, the Germans are coming. What shall we do?"

Margery knew what to do; they practised emergency drill at the hospital and the first rule was to keep calm. Mum's breaking that one already, Margery thought. Their neighbour, Alf, came round wearing his Home Guard uniform and his tin hat.

"Lock your doors and stay inside," he said, handing Margery a stout stick. "Use this if you have to."

They sat at the kitchen table and Margery saw her hands trembling, felt her heart fluttering. Nellie reached up and took the tea caddy from its shelf to make a pot of tea and then another and many, many more as they had sat there hour after hour, nerves taut, tummies churning. Margery wished she knew what was happening. Then she thought it was better not to know; it might be bad news. Just before dawn, Alf came back.

"False alarm, no Germans, no invasion; it was just some bodies washed up on the beaches – from the Channel Islands probably. All's well now." Thank God that's over, thought Margery; she went to bed and dropped into an uneasy sleep until the alarm clock woke her for her morning shift, a busy shift at the best of times.

She rubbed her eyes when she came off duty; she was exhausted and would be glad to get home for a quiet sit down but, as she walked into the kitchen, she heard voices from the sitting room. Bother, she thought, I'm too tired for visitors. She walked across the hall and into the sitting room. Donald got up from an armchair by the fireplace to greet her.

"Hello Margery. I've got a few days leave so I thought I'd come over to see how you folks were doing."

Margery had hardly seen him since he joined the RAF and she welcomed the chance to catch up. She had known Donald since childhood; their families were friends. Margery sat on the sofa opposite Donald who was by the French windows. Nellie heaved herself to her feet.

"If you'll excuse me, Donald, I'm going to get my hat and pop down to the shop." Margery knew it was just an excuse to leave them alone.

"Your mother has been telling me about Jack," Donald said. "I'm so sorry. He was a good old boy."

Margery remembered that Donald had been with them when they first collected Jack. Johnnie had persuaded him to drive to the station all those years ago and, while she rode Jack along the narrow lane, Donald had driven behind, his headlamps casting shadows on the road across the common. Those memories linked them, a thread weaving through their shared past.

"I hated to do it but it wasn't fair to keep him now the war's really on." Margery looked carefully at the floor and felt the now familiar stab of pain; she concentrated on stopping her lips from quivering and pulled herself together with an effort.

"Tell me your news, Donald. What have you been up to?"

"Oh this and that. I'm in Bomber Command but our boys in the Spitfires have got their hands full keeping the Luftwaffe at bay. The Germans won't invade unless they can command the skies. It's all about air cover, you know."

Margery didn't but she nodded all the same.

"We see so many enemy bombers going over, almost every night."

"Yes, you're not far from Farnborough and that's bound to be a target. It's the bases and factories, they're after."

"A German plane came down in the village. I'm taking Brian's nephew to see the wreck."

"He'll enjoy that. I heard about that prang." Donald paused and offered Margery a cigarette but she shook her head. "You still don't smoke then?" Margery shook her head. Donald lit his cigarette, took a pull and blew out a smoke ring.

"Tell me about you," he said. "Your mother says you're working at Brookwood Hospital."

"Yes, we're looking after the boys who were wounded at Dunkirk."

"It was a bad show, that one," said Donald. "We underestimated Hitler and his *Blitzkrieg.*"

She knew that Donald could talk politics and military strategy till the cows came home; Johnnie said he was a serious thinker but to Margery he was just a dull boy. Donald paused and looked at Margery. "Your mother said Brian's not back from France."

The grief made her head spin and the tears pricked. Would she ever get used to it? She hated folks feeling sorry for her; she wanted to hide the hurt. Why did Mum have to tell? She knew she must keep her chin up but the anguish for Brian and for Jack was unbearable.

"No, he's not back," she said. "I keep hoping I'll hear... but there's nothing so far." Donald looked at her and touched her arm.

"I'll remember you – and him – in my prayers." He

paused for a moment. "It looks like you need cheering up. Would you like to come to the flicks with me one evening? It's *All This and Heaven Too* with Bette Davis." Margery hesitated. Would it be disloyal to Brian to go out with Donald? "Just as friends, Margery, old friends."

"Yes, I'd like that. Thank you for asking."

"All right. I'll pick you up the day after tomorrow, about six."

Margery drove the governess cart to drop Doris and little John at the bus stop; she waited for them to clamber aboard the bus and waved them on their way. She had enjoyed their visit and would have been glad for them to stay longer but Doris said it was time to go home; John must get ready to go back to school and, besides, Hether had been alone long enough.

Margery stopped and Joey put his head down to eat the grass. This was their spot, their favourite spot where Brian had first kissed her. She'd fetched him from the bus and they'd stopped to look at the view, the heather, the gorse and the silver birch trees so characteristic of this beautiful heathland. Then he'd leaned forward, closer, closer until their lips had touched, tentatively at first, then eagerly, passionately making her head spin, her skin tingle. That was the beginning of their courtship, their love and after that they'd always stopped here to kiss and remember.

But she couldn't linger today. She must get back; the Vicar was coming to tea. She pulled Joey's head up and clicked to him. They returned to the road and Joey trotted off. She had taken little John to see the wreck of the German bomber and had struggled to answer his questions.

She could have done with Donald and his expertise. Little boys relished technical details; the make, the model of the plane, its flight speed, its bomb capacity fascinated John but baffled Margery. It was as if they were talking different languages. But pets were common ground; John loved Judy and Joey but he wasn't allowed animals at home – Hether was allergic, Doris said.

Margery liked Doris, Brian's older sister by ten years, who had mothered him. Amy had been absorbed with her last child, sickly little Stella, so Doris had been the one to wipe Brian's face, kiss him better and read him his bedtime story. She was a great comfort to Margery as she was the one person who never doubted that he was going to come back… never for a moment.

"I'd know, you see, if something had happened to him. I'm sure I would. You'll hear soon, Margery. Keep your fingers crossed," Doris said.

Margery must hurry to get back in time for Rev Smythe. He wanted to talk about Brian, of course. Their wedding Banns – the ones that had been read back in May and were good for three months – were about to expire. But Brian wasn't back, still wasn't back, and she had to keep hoping; it was all she could do.

CHAPTER 15

France, 29th May 1940

Sharp guttural shouts and tramping feet woke Brian. He lay still, uncertain where he was. He felt stiff and uncomfortable; he seemed to be lying in a field curled up between two other men. Then he remembered; they had surrendered, been captured by the Germans and marched to this field. After that, all he had wanted to do was sleep. For the past two weeks he had been running on adrenaline, short on sleep, short on food, nerves taut, keeping going and then… he had felt limp, had lain down and slept. They all had, Elliot, John, Mills, Jackson and the others; no-one had stirred all night.

As he lay there, the details of the previous day came back to him and his heart raced; he was thankful to be alive. The battle, the fire, the crash as the building fell just after they left it and then that wall. Thank goodness Elliot had called that senior officer. Who knows what would have happened otherwise? After that the Germans had helped the medics to move the wounded from the cellars, carrying them out through the rubble and the dust.

Elliot had been right to surrender; he'd had no other option. But what had happened to the others? He remembered the bodies he had seen lying in the street. One of them was Major Heyworth, for sure; he had been a brave man, risking his life to find ammunition. It must have been a sniper's bullet. Another body looked horribly familiar, lying on his front, arms above his head, one leg crooked up, the other straight. Brian had seen that posture every morning in his billet. Brian had looked but had to go on marching, keeping in step as the Germans hurried them along. He couldn't investigate, couldn't be sure.

Brian stood up and stretched, aching in every joint. He went over to the hedge to pee. A light mist rose from the land and a blackbird sang in the oak tree on the other side of the hedge, the side where freedom lay. In the distance he could see people moving about, civilians not soldiers. They went about their daily business, as if today was just an ordinary day. But for him, nothing was normal. Capture was not what he had expected.

Guards stood by the gate and at every corner, their guns cocked and ready to shoot if anyone tried to escape. But the prisoners were stunned, like zombies, overwhelmed by what had happened; they didn't think of making a run for it, not yet. His men began to wake up and they looked bewildered, lost; they were only boys and he was their officer; he was responsible for them. He'd better buck them up.

"How are you doing, lads?"

"Not bad, Sir," said Taylor. "But what 'appens next?"

"Breakfast, I think." Brian saw the Germans setting up a camp kitchen. It wasn't much, just stale bread and coffee – at least, they said it was coffee although it smelled like dirty dishwater. There were no cups and prisoners were lining up, some of them using their tin hats as receptacles. Brian noticed a stack of empty cans lying near the hedge; he grabbed several and distributed them amongst his men.

"Share them, boys, so everyone can drink and hang on to them." The coffee tasted bitter and gritty, like the mud on the school rugger pitch; Brian's mouth was sour and dry. He ran his hand over his chin, noting the stubble. How long was it since he'd shaved? Two days, three days perhaps?

Then he remembered that his shaving kit had been in his kitbag, in 'the Keep', along with his clothes, his pyjamas, his greatcoat, everything. I've lost it all in the fire.

Then it hit him: Margery's photo, Margery's last letter, his little mementos, they had been there too. He had nothing left and he felt bereft without anything personal to link him to her. How would she know what had happened? How could he get word to her? He felt as if a current was carrying him away from her out to sea; his self-control was unravelling. Then Elliot put his hand on his shoulder.

"Brian, we're bound to be questioned today. We need to go around and remind the men of the form. They must only give their name, rank, number and regiment – nothing else. Can you get the word round?"

"Of course." Brian pulled himself together and remembered his duty. "I'll talk to John and the other lieutenants; we can go around the men. It's good to have something to do." So, he moved amongst the men, reminding them, sustaining them and keeping their spirits up. It was the best he could do.

They were taken to the German headquarters, questioned and registered. As Brian gave his father's name as next of kin, he realised that he'd been captured on the very day he and Margery had planned for their wedding; if it had gone ahead, Margery would have been his next-of-kin. He became *Kriegsgefangen Nummer 765* and held up a board with his number as his mugshot was taken, like a common criminal. He felt humiliated, as if he had done something wrong but he had done what every soldier should, obeyed orders and fought hard. He felt like he was whirling towards… the bottom.

"Will our relatives be informed?" he asked.

"*Jawohl. Das Rotes Kreuz.*"

The Red Cross thought Brian; I hope they get a move on. After registration they were marched to a holding camp behind the front line. There were rolls of barbed wire around the area and armed guards on every gate. When Brian arrived, the camp already held hundreds of French prisoners; it seemed as if the whole French Army had been captured. Belgian and Dutch soldiers mingled with the British, men and officers alike.

The Bucks contingent huddled together at night, keeping warm like birds roosting on a branch; at mealtimes they made sure everyone got a share of the rations, poor though they were. There was strength in numbers, especially as more prisoners thronged into the camp until there was barely a corner left to sleep in. Brian noticed two familiar faces amongst the new arrivals: Rupert and Sandy; they'd both been fighting on the perimeter of Hazebrouck.

"Hello, there. When did you get here?"

"We've just come in, old boy," said Rupert. "When the Germans broke through our lines, I sent my men off in small groups and told them to make for the coast, cross country. I thought they might have a chance that way. My little group didn't get far; we were picked up by the church and here we are. What happened to you lot?"

"Well, we were in 'the Keep' of course…" Brian said and he summarised their story for Rupert.

"Who else is here?"

"Oh Elliot, John and a few others. We were all taken together… in the nun's garden." Rupert nodded.

"What about Simon? Is he here?" Brian hesitated before he answered.

"No, he decided to try his luck the other way, out into the side street and… I'm not sure he made it." Brian found it hard to think of Simon, his constant good humour and his wife, with an infant on the way. He must leave that for later; he couldn't bear it now. Rupert laid his hand on Brian's arm.

"Bad show, old boy."

Each new batch of prisoners brought news, vital news about the progress of the war. The evacuation from Dunkirk was going well, better than anyone could have expected, but they were only taking men; transport and equipment was left behind, strewn across the beaches like seaweed.

"They say there's not much left of the British Army," said Rupert. "It'll be hard for old Winnie to crack on after this."

Brian noted Churchill's nickname. He was Prime Minister now; he'd heard that as they marched back through Belgium.

After a few days in the holding camp, the routine was broken. As soon as breakfast was served, they were told to form up in two columns, officers in one and other ranks in the second. The guards were tense, edgy, poking them with their rifles.

"What the dickens is this?" Brian asked Elliot as he watched the men from his company line up without him.

"It's the usual practice under the Geneva Convention," said Elliot. "They always separate officers from men, to clarify the chain of command. You know, it could be difficult if you were telling your men to do something that contradicted the German orders. It'd be hard for everyone."

"But they're *my* men." Brian bit his nails as the order was given and Taylor, Mills and Jackson started to march. He'd been with these lads since they left England five months ago; they were his responsibility and now he was leaving them to… who knew what?

"See you after the war, Sir," called Mills, with a faint replica of his cheeky grin. As his men marched, under guard, out of the gates, Brian felt hollow but there was no time to brood; the guards were yelling at him to move and he had to crack on. The officers marched out, taking a left turn instead of a right. They went by different routes but they were all going east… towards Germany.

France, June 1940

The long columns of men wound through the villages and towns of northern France. Everywhere they saw the scars of recent fighting, the shell holes, the burnt-out buildings, the piles of rubble. There were animals wandering aimlessly, thin scraggy dogs and bellowing cows, their udders distended. The column of prisoners passed close to Wahagnies and Brian remembered the Easter party, those church parades, the battalion marching with their heads held high. Now they were a raggle-taggle crew, unwashed, unshaved, with pangs of hunger as a constant companion. They came to a village, a grimy column of skeletons in British Army uniform and the French women came out of their houses.

"*Les Anglais,*" they said, gasping and bringing their hands up to their mouths.

"*Nous avons faim.*" The officers held out their hands

and mimed eating. They rubbed their stomachs. The women brought out bread and cheese and ran along giving them to the marching prisoners. We were sent here to protect these people, Brian thought, but now we're begging from them. The German guards circled the column on bicycles, their rifles on their shoulders. Brian knew they wouldn't hesitate to fire; two stragglers had already been shot.

"*'Raus, 'raus, Englander,*" they shouted as they urged them on for three hours at a time.

"Crikey," said Brian. "I thought I was used to marching but not like this." The British Army took a break every two hours.

"Their practices are different from ours," said Rupert. "Besides, take a look at them. These guards are older than the Jerries who captured us, the fighting men. They're probably veterans from the Great War and they've got scores to settle with British Tommies."

Brian's mouth was dry, his lips cracked; he hadn't had a drink since breakfast and the sun shone down relentlessly. He felt light-headed. They came to a village where the women put out buckets of water. Brian ran to one, cupping the water in his hands. The guard rode up, stuck his leg out and knocked the buckets over, like skittles. Brian clenched his fists and went red in the face.

"That's so bloody unnecessary. It wouldn't hurt to let me have a drop of water." Brian felt Rupert's hand on his shoulder.

"Move on, old boy. It won't help to fly off the handle."

Brian could see the wisdom of these words but how could Rupert be so unflappable?

"Think about it. If we're thirsty, we're less likely to run

for it. It's their orders and it makes their job easier," Rupert said.

"Keep going, you two," said Elliot coming up beside them. They've got their eye on you. Remember those route marches, Brian? Old B-B trained us for marching, didn't he?"

"I bet the old boy didn't think we'd be marching to Jerry's tune." Brian made an effort and pulled himself together. With Elliot and Rupert beside him he marched on, and on, and on until night fell.

They slept in makeshift quarters, a barn, a field, the grandstand at a racecourse. Brian liked sleeping in the grandstand; at least they had a roof over their heads. Every day he marched, further and further east, away from the Channel, from home, from Margery. Did she know that he was captured, that he was still alive? The Germans said the Red Cross would inform relatives but they hadn't seen the Red Cross. Brian thought of the pain he was causing Margery but he felt so muddle-headed that nothing was clear. He couldn't think about it; he must get through this.

Food was scarce, for guards and for prisoners, so they scavenged the countryside. Brian saw a storage clamp, the mound rising like a tomb by the side of a field where the farmer had stacked his root vegetables. He ate them greedily, dirt, peel and all; at last he had something in his stomach. Then the cramps began, at first a twinge, then an urgent pain and, with a nod from the guard, Brian rushed for the ditch, slipping his braces off his shoulders. He saw John was there too, groaning beside him, his trousers round his knees. He looked in bad shape, thin with an unearthly sheen on his face, like stagnant water.

"Come on, John," said Brian, when they were finished. "We must crack on."

"I don't think I can. My legs are all wobbly and I feel sick."

"I know, but you must. Here, give me your arm and we'll get along together." Brian remembered John as a bright platoon leader but they none of them looked too bright now.

After a week on the road, they came to a river and continued by barge into Germany. They halted briefly at a transit camp and the officers were issued with a pre-printed postcard to send to their relatives. It read:

I am in German captivity and am quite allright/am slightly wounded. Brian crossed out the words 'am slightly wounded',

I shall be transferred from here to a permanent camp and will send you the new address later. There I shall be allowed to write again and receive your mail.

There was a space for his name, rank, regiment, the date and his signature. Brian filled the card in, dated it 14th June 1940 and addressed it to Margery.

Then they marched to the railway station and crowded into cattle trucks. The doors clattered and Brian heard a thump as a wooden bar slotted into place. The wagons were dark and the only light filtered in through the slatted wooden sides. Stale bread and water were thrown in and Brian noticed a bucket in the corner. Off they went by rail on the last leg of their journey. After two days in the wagon, the smell of vomit, shit and fear was all pervasive; Brian stayed as far from the bucket as he could.

"Hang on, Brian, hang on Rupert," said Elliot, pale and sick himself but still supporting the others. "We'll soon be there." But where was 'there', Brian wondered?

Hamburg, 1964

We sat in the drawing room before dinner, my family and their family together. I was on my gap year, an au pair girl to a German family. My charges, the children, were in bed and their parents – my employers – had invited my parents to dinner. Grandfather completed the party. I had been there for three months but I had not mentioned the war. You didn't.

The small talk danced around seeking common ground as we perched on the stiff horsehair chairs in the long light drawing room. We talked about their divided country, about the Wall through Berlin, about the Iron Curtain, separating families and friends. Those topics united us against a common enemy. My father tried to speak German, using some of the phrases he had learned twenty years before.

"It's polite to speak German as we're in their country," he said. My mother had no such scruples; she made do with English, spoken loudly and slowly. The Germans spoke perfect English. The children's grandfather had been married to an American, one of his many wives, and English – or American English – was the language of business.

"Where did you learn your German?" my employer asked. I held my breath, wondering what my father would say. He was picking an invisible fleck off his jacket.

"Well," he said. "I was in Germany throughout the

war. You see, I was in the British Army and was captured at Dunkirk."

Their faces stiffened, as they sat upright in their seats, tense, unsure. Then Grandfather clapped his hands down on his knees.

"You were captured at Dunkirk? Did they march you through France in a long column, with guards on bikes pedalling round like sheepdogs?" He traced circles in the air with his hands.

"Yes, they did. It was a bit like herding sheep, I suppose."

"'Raus, 'raus, Englander'," Grandfather said, smiling. "I was one of those guards."

The rest of the family held their breath, uncertain. My father's face lit up in recognition of their shared experience, their memories.

"It's a small world, isn't it? What a coincidence."

"I think we gave you Tommies a pretty hard time, kicking over those water buckets, eh?" The old man shook his head and peered into my father's face. "No hard feelings?"

"No, no hard feelings. You were soldiers, obeying orders, just as we were. It was different days, different ways."

CHAPTER 16

Germany, June 1940

The train stopped, the doors rattled and Brian blinked as the light came streaming into his wagon. He heard the now familiar words:

"*'Raus, 'raus, Englander.*" They marched from the station into the town and the German people lined the streets to stare at the British officers. At the bottom of the hill, Brian saw the watchtower, stark against the sky. This is it, he thought, our destination; thank God I've got here – but where am I?

"This must be Laufen," Elliot said. "It's near the Austrian border."

Brian was weak with dysentery; his head felt heavy, his legs leaden as he lined up with the others in the courtyard. Those last two days in the wagon – just a cattle-truck really – were truly wretched, the stench of the latrine bucket, the stomach cramps and the jolting of the train. He looked up at the building, their prison, five storeys high. He saw peeling paint, piles of debris and a rat skulking around the edge of the yard. A German officer marched towards them, flanked by his entourage. The light glinted on their cap badges, the German eagle.

"It's the Camp Commandant." said Elliot. "He's going to address us." The commandant spoke in English, accented English.

"You cannot escape. If you try to escape, you will be SHOT." The officers jeered and heckled like impudent schoolboys. Then they marched to the bath house. That's a jolly good idea, Brian thought. I've been three weeks in this battledress with no chance to wash or shave; I've grown a monster beard and I itch. John was scratching beside him, and Rupert; they were all lousy. Their heads were shaved, like convicts. I suppose it's the only way to get the dirt off, Brian thought. He left the bath house beside a tall young man, who smiled down shyly.

"I see they've left your moustache," he said.

Brian ran his hand over his head, then stroked his upper lip.

"Mmm. I'm rather glad about that; it took me a long time to grow."

"It looks strange, though – no hair, no beard and then a moustache. I'm Bob, by the way, Captain Bob Smith from the East Riding Yeomanry."

"I'm Captain Brian Dowling, 1st Bucks Battalion." Brian's interest in people quickened, like a spark in the night. "I was taken at Hazebrouck. What about you?"

"Cassel."

"The rest of our brigade went to Cassel. I suppose your lot provided the artillery cover?"

"Yes. We hid the guns in a wood, outside a little place called *Le Coucou*," said Bob.

"How long were you there – at *Le Coucou*?" Brian remembered Cuckoo Hill where he had ridden with Margery.

"About a week. A couple of days setting up before Jerry got there. Then four or five days fighting."

"You did well. We only lasted two days."

"We did our best to stop them; we had the advantage of the higher ground but there were just too damned many of them. They brought up the Luftwaffe, the tanks, artillery, infantry, the whole works."

"Yes, it was the same with us." Brian remembered the endless waves of tanks shelling 'the Keep'. The guards snapped out orders and put an end to their conversation. They took the officers to their quarters by rank. Brian was the only captain in his party and he felt bereft as his Bucks Battalion comrades were sent to different rooms. He was glad Bob remained beside him. Brian's legs wobbled and black spots danced before his eyes as he struggled up the stairs. I must hang on, I mustn't faint. I'm glad my room is on the first floor; I don't think I'd make it any higher.

He looked out of the window at the mountains and noticed that the darkness of fir trees contrasted with the bright green of the chestnuts. It's a wonderful outlook, he thought, but beautiful views out there can't make up for the dirt and squalor in here; it's downright seedy.

The room held 64 officers, all crowded together. There were Scotsmen in kilts, infantrymen, and cavalry officers in a variety of uniforms. The bunks were stacked three tiers high around the walls, and in the middle of the room stood tables, with chairs and benches. He smelled wet washing, cooking… and feet. Bile rose in Brian's mouth; this is it, he thought, where we eat, sleep, cook, everything. He and Bob gravitated towards two empty bunks.

"You take the top one," said Brian, looking at Bob's long legs. "I'll be happy in the middle."

He noticed their roommates lounging on their beds gazing at the ceiling or the bunk above. He collapsed on his bunk, with its straw mattress and one thin blanket. Captivity feels shameful, like a punishment, he thought, and I'm a prisoner for the duration of the war, a sentence without a time limit.

In the camp Brian was cut off from news. I haven't the foggiest idea how the fighting is going; none of us has – except the guards. When Brian went to the latrines, he was stopped by a guard.

"*London in sechs Wochen,*" he said, "London in six weeks." He leered as he gestured to show that the German Army would loot and rape its way across England. Is it true, Brian thought? Have the Germans reached English soil? There's not much to stop them. But what's happening to Margery, to my parents, my sisters? I've been a bit of a flop; I haven't been able to protect them.

"*England kaput,*" jeered the guard, the next time Brian ventured from his room. He said Britain had surrendered. I do hope that's not true, thought Brian; much as I long to go home to Margery, I don't want the war to end that way. Surely that old warhorse Churchill wouldn't wave the white flag. Brian didn't know what to believe and returned to the room tight-lipped and white faced.

Tom, the man on the bunk below, looked at him and said: "We call them *latrinograms,* old boy. It always happens if they get us alone. They love tormenting us." Tom had been captured at Calais and had arrived in Laufen a fortnight earlier.

"Rotten buggers! Tell me now, what's the form in the camp?"

"There's nothing much going on, nothing much at all. The only thing we *have* to do is turn up for *Appell*, the roll call, at nine o'clock every morning. That's when they count us to make sure we're all still here."

"What about rations?" Brian's trousers were hanging limp, only kept up by his braces. He struggled to recall the Geneva Convention; surely, the Germans had to feed them?

"We get precious little, I'm afraid. Coffee – if you can call it that – for breakfast, watery soup and bread at noon, and soup again with a few rotten potatoes for our evening meal. That's about it. And watch out for your bread; they'll diddle you if they can – and I don't mean the guards."

Brian felt uneasy, like a new boy at school; but at least he had Bob. We have a lot in common, he thought; we're the same age and were Territorials, not full-time soldiers. Before the war Bob had been working in the family business – the timber trade, he called it. Brian found Bob an easy companion; he listened attentively and had plenty of quiet common sense. They were both diffident in large groups but enjoyed a laugh together over a subtle joke or an amusing incident. They began to look out for each other.

It was an effort getting up in the morning; Brian's limbs felt heavy, his mind vacant. There seemed no reason to leave his hard bunk, no purpose to the day, nothing. But his morning routine was the string binding him together, fending off anguish, despair, disintegration. So he heaved himself up and went to the bath house while Bob lay lounging on his top bunk.

When Brian returned, Bob was on his feet beside Pat. Brian knew Pat by sight, a small man with thin hair and a sandy moustache. He had tried to avoid him; he seemed unsavoury, like the school sneak. Bob had drawn himself up to his full height, his face set hard as he glared down at Pat.

"Brian, is this your blanket? Pat here says it's his." Pat

sidled up to Brian.

"Yes, old boy, don't you remember? I lent it to you yesterday." Brian looked at the blanket, coarse and grey, the one he had bought with his camp pay to fend off the cold mountain air.

"No, you didn't." Brian pursed his lips and shook his head. "This one's definitely mine. Look here, it's got my name on it." There in the middle of the blanket was a Cash's name tape saying 'Brian Arthur Dowling' in black capital letters.

"Oh, frightfully sorry, old boy. My mistake. It must have been someone else." Pat slunk off. It is like school, Brian thought, remembering how the other boys would take your PE kit and would be most apologetic when, smarting from your punishment, you found them out.

"Thanks, Bob. You saved my bacon. He'd have made off with it without you."

"It's nothing," said Bob. "But that's a good trick, sewing your name into the middle."

"Yes. It'd make a bloody big hole if they cut it off." I need a friend in a place like this, Brian thought. He told Bob about Margery and found more common ground; he was also engaged – to Norah.

"We were going to get married on my first leave," said Brian.

"Our plans hadn't got as far as that."

"We had the invitations out, the Banns read, the church booked and everything." Brian ached to think of those plans, so lovingly made; he felt guilty for disappointing Margery, for causing her pain. But now he was in a camp, at least he could write to her; two letters and two postcards a month, those were the rules.

"I can't tell you what a relief it is to be able to write to Margery again." Brian sat at the table, his pencil in his hand, thinking how best to fill that thin airmail form. Bob chewed his pencil.

"It's hard though to tell them anything meaningful. The censor would just black it out."

"I suppose so." Brian's forehead creased in a frown. "We don't want to make it sound too grim or they'll worry."

"My card sounds a bit like a holiday postcard. You know 'sunny days and beautiful scenery'."

"But not 'wish you were here', I hope?"

"No, definitely not that."

"I said we had air pie for dinner again today," said Tom.

"That's a good one," said Brian. "That might get past the censor."

Laufen, July 1940

"It's hard to fill the time, isn't it?" said Bob, as they strolled back to the room after *Appell.*

"Yes," said Brian. "I suppose it's a cushy life. I never thought I'd miss work but I feel a bit lost without the structure it gave me."

The days seemed endless, a long straight road going nowhere. There was too much time to think, to delve into those dark recesses where he'd pushed the painful memories. He gazed out of the window at the mountains, their mood ever-changing. This morning he thought they looked black, foreboding, the fir trees pointing upwards like dark, jagged teeth.

His thoughts turned back to Simon. We shared good

times at those pre-war summer camps, at Newbury when we were training, in Wahagnies sharing a billet and that day we went to Lille; we had a grand meal that day and the champagne was top notch. Simon was such a chum but now he's gone; I had to leave him in that street in Hazebrouck, outside 'the Keep'. How I miss him! It was bitter to think that Simon would never hold his baby in his arms, never know whether it was a boy or a girl, never watch its first tottering steps. He had been denied those simple pleasures, denied a future. Brian mourned the loss of his friend.

He thought back to that moment in 'the Keep', that split second decision, when Simon had asked him to go with him. It was just chance; I might easily have gone over that wall, and then I would have caught that sniper's bullet. Then again, I might have been trapped in 'the Keep' when the flames caught hold or shot in the nuns' garden. But I wasn't; I survived and Simon didn't, Martin didn't, Heyworth didn't. Those thoughts made Brian realise how lucky he was. I hate it here but it's better than the alternative; at least I am alive. I've got a future, a life with Margery, and children if we're blessed. We're both young and we've got so much to look forward to… after the war. That's the thing to hang on to.

"Oh, there you are, Brian," said Elliot, strolling over to his bunk. "How are you doing?"

"All right, I suppose." He'd keep his dark thoughts to himself; that was the way it was in Laufen, each man locked in his own personal hell.

"I wondered whether you'd care to come to the lecture, this morning?" Elliot said. "It's about birds. We're all going from the Bucks." It'll be something to do, Brian thought, and it'll be good to see my mates; there were seven of them there now.

"Right-ho." Brian stood up slowly to avoid dizziness; he was still weak. They made their way downstairs to join a group sitting around waiting. John was there with David and Bill, who had come in the day before yesterday; their heads were slumped on their chests, their hands hanging by their sides, their eyes staring vacantly ahead. They look like ghosts, thought Brian.

"Where's Rupert?"

"Oh, he's busy; he's got other things to do," said Elliot.

Brian had seen Rupert once or twice with another officer, strolling around the camp, talking earnestly together. He's made new friends, Brian thought.

"By the way, Brian, you play bridge, don't you?" Brian's thoughts returned to the sitting room at Stone Cottage, the curtain drawn across the middle and the card table pulled up by the fire, the horse brasses glinting, as he sat down with Johnnie, Margery and Nellie to make up a four. Cards had been frowned upon in the Dowling household, like betting and alcohol, but Brian had been more than willing to be Margery's bridge partner.

"Yes, I have played."

"Good. Perhaps you'd care to join us tomorrow evening? We're going to have a bit of a tournament. Chin up, old man."

"Right-ho." Good old Elliot, Brian thought; he's still looking after us chaps from the Bucks.

The speaker started talking about the bird life in and around the camp. He explained that the trees provided plenty of cover and the river attracted waterfowl. The redstart, he said, was nesting down by the water and he was thinking of studying its behaviour. Brian thought how strange it was that the birds were free to come and go across the wire, backwards and forwards at will. I'm used to seeing chickens in a coop or canaries in a cage, but now it's us in the bag.

"I'm glad I came," said Brian.

"Yes," said Elliot. "It's a bit like reading a good book; it takes you into a different world. By the way, did you know we're starting a library?"

"That's a good idea. I'll look forward to it." I suppose the days are passing, Brian thought; it's seven weeks and four days now since I was captured and sometimes it's almost reasonable in here. The sun shone on the mountains, highlighting the bare peaks and the wooded valleys. Those mountains change as fast as my mood, thought Brian.

"What was the lecture like?" Bob asked.

"Quite interesting actually. The 'Professor' certainly knew his stuff – a real expert, I'd say. They've got one on farming tomorrow. Shall we go together?" After that Bob and Brian became regular attendees at the 'University of Laufen'; they said it was an institution which was easier to get into than to leave!

Brian and Bob lay in the hot sun and rested, their bodies getting browner every day. They had nothing to do and nowhere to go; each day was like the last, unvarying, like beads on a string. They sat in the shade of the lime tree by the river, their backs resting against the rough stone wall of the castle courtyard. A blackbird sang, his notes trilling over the wire and they watched the shadows chasing across the mountains, moving like quicksilver. The air felt thick, pressing down on them.

"If only Margery were here and I were free, we could have a grand time wandering around on the tracks up there in the woods." Brian missed her more than words could tell but he had received no letters; no-one had. News filtered into the camp only from new arrivals. There was no sign of the war ending yet and Brian began to worry.

"I'll soon be home on leave," he had told Margery last Christmas. "We'll get married then." He hadn't expected capture and an open-ended sentence. Was it reasonable, he pondered, to hold her to her Boxing Day promise?

"You know, Bob, I've been thinking about Margery."

"I think about Norah all the time, too."

"I have been wondering whether it's fair to expect her to wait for me."

"I know what you mean, but surely… it's up to them, isn't it? Up to the girls to make that decision?" Brian's face was set and unsmiling as he gazed across the river.

"I am thinking of coming out with it … sort of telling her in a letter that she is free, if that's what she wants, if that would make her happy." Brian's voice was shaky and he was looking resolutely away from Bob, towards those darkening mountains. Bob turned towards his friend, his forehead creasing in a frown.

"But, Brian, that would make you so unhappy… if she were to choose…" Bob's voice trailed away; he couldn't say the words.

"Yes, I know. But you see, I love her so much. She's always been the only one for me. But… when I proposed to her, I wanted to look after her, to make her happy." Brian hesitated, searching for words. "I went to France to protect her, to keep her safe. But I couldn't. And now I must be causing her distress, pain even."

"I see your point." Bob stroked his chin. "It must be hard for the girls at home, waiting and waiting with no news. You're right; they must fear the worst. But to write a letter like that…"

"I could tell her that… if she could find love elsewhere, then I'd be content." Brian's face was set, concentrating hard on the woods beyond the wire. "I think that's the right word, 'content', because I wouldn't be happy; I'd be very *un*happy, as you said. But I'd be… sort of satisfied knowing that she was happy."

"Are you sure, Brian?" Bob was peering at his friend.

"No, I'm not sure." Brian was still gazing into the distance, his eyes half-shut. "I'm just turning it over in my mind. But I am coming around to thinking it's the right thing to do."

"It would certainly be a brave thing to do," said Bob. "A very brave thing, indeed."

"Maybe." Brian turned to face Bob. "I'll give it some more thought. Thanks for listening. My father was always good at listening to my troubles when I was growing up and I sort of got used to talking things through."

The following Tuesday Brian put his feelings down on paper and wrote that 'brave' letter. He put it in the postbag and the guards took it to the censor. That was it; the die was cast.

"I'm not sure our letters are leaving the camp," said Bob, a few days later. "There seem to be sacks of mail in that storeroom waiting for collection. I don't think the Red Cross have got the postal service organised yet."

"Maybe not," said Brian, thinking of that fateful letter. "But they will go eventually, won't they?" All he could do was wait and with every week it became harder and harder to write. Brian didn't know what Margery was doing, what she was thinking, how she viewed their relationship. He couldn't write about their circle of friends – Johnnie, Norah, Fleda and Donald – as he didn't know what had happened to them; it was wartime after all. But camp life was like a compass pattern, arc within arc, ever the same. He was running out of material for his weekly letters.

Laufen, August 1940

Elliot walked into Brian's room and invited him to a 'little dinner party' for the battalion.

"There's ten of us here now, old boy. We'll all bring our own rations and we'll have a whip round for some wine."

Brian knew that some of the guards were prepared to go shopping for the officers, provided they were rewarded for their trouble. Six bottles of a good Moselle were purchased. Brian walked to Elliot's room as the late afternoon sunshine picked out the colours on the mountains. They sat on benches round the table while Elliot's roommates sat on their bunks. Elliot was a major so his room was better than Brian's – but not much better. Brian's cabbage soup and potatoes tasted better, washed down with several tin cups of wine and it was good to chat with his battalion comrades.

"What have you been up to Rupert? I haven't seen you at the University of Laufen."

"No, not my bag of tricks, old boy." Rupert stroked his handlebar moustache. "I've been snooping around the camp, getting the feel of the place and seeing what the Goons are up to."

"Goons?" Brian thought of the cartoon characters. "That's a new one on me. I like it; it cuts those guards down to size." The officers were beginning to develop their own slang, their badge of belonging; they were forging a group identity within the camp. They referred to themselves as *Kriegies,* from the German word for prisoner of war, *Kriegsgefangener.*

"By the way, Brian, I've been meaning to ask you. You're a short chap aren't you?" Rupert was over six feet tall and, beside him, Brian felt small indeed. "You can't fill your bunk. You wouldn't miss a few of your bed boards, would you, old boy?"

"Well, I guess I could let you have a couple. But what do you want them for?"

"Oh, just a little scheme of mine." Rupert smiled at Brian, who knew his charm disguised a lively mind. I wonder what he's up to, he thought. He turned to Bill on his other side. He had always been daring, treating his soldiering like a big adventure.

"Tell me about your travels. I hear you had quite an exciting time after you left Hazebrouck."

"Well, you remember I was with B Company fighting along the railway. When the Germans overran our positions, we broke up into small groups, making for Dunkirk. My lot came across a farmer who gave us some bread and cheese and let us sleep in his barn. We tried to travel at night and sleep by day and…" Bill went on with his story while Brian sipped his wine. "...but one night we walked right into a Jerry patrol"

"And they brought you here, like the rest of us."

"Yes, that's about it."

"I'm glad you're feeling better now, David," said Brian. The young lieutenant had been wounded in 'the Keep' and Brian had seen him led away from the nuns' garden between two German orderlies.

"Yes, it wasn't much, just a flesh wound. The Jerries patched me up and sent me here. It's a grand idea this dinner party and I'm enjoying the wine."

"The Moselle was Rupert's choice," said Elliot.

"Those vineyards on the southerly slopes can usually be relied upon," said Rupert, squinting carefully at the wine in his tin cup, swirling it around and sniffing. "What shall we toast?"

"Oh, I think it must be the King," said Elliot and they all raised their cups.

"How about 'Home by Christmas'?" Rupert raised his eyebrows and twirled his moustache. "My wife and daughters will be expecting me and I'd hate to disappoint my girls." Laughing, they all drank again. Surely he can't think we'll win the war by Christmas, thought Brian? I wonder whether he's planning...? But Brian kept his thoughts to himself as he made his way back to his room before lights out.

A few weeks later, Brian noticed that three British orderlies had dressed in officers' uniform and were lining up for the officers' *Appell*. I wonder what this is all about, Brian thought. The Goons counted the prisoners.

"Zehn... Zwanzig... Dreizig... Vierzig..." They had to make the numbers tally. It's a bit like cashing up at the bank, Brian thought, to make the books balance. The *Kriegies* shuffled around in their lines and called out random numbers in German; it was all part of the game to harass the guards, making their job as hard as possible. The more men Hitler deployed to guard the camps, the fewer there were on the frontline. But today the SBO, the Senior British Officer, was signalling an early end to their pranks. He must have a reason, Brian thought. When they had been dismissed, Brian wandered over to Elliot.

"What's up, then?"

"It's Rupert and his friends. They've dug a tunnel and gone. Keep it to yourself, though. We want to keep it from the Goons as long as possible, to give them a head start you see."

So he wanted the bed boards to prop up his tunnel, thought Brian. He felt like punching the air; he was so pleased. Rupert had outwitted the Goons and shown that escape was possible. Perhaps *he* would be home for Christmas.

CHAPTER 17

England, 31st August 1940

Margery stretched and yawned; she was having a lie-in. She didn't often get one but she was off duty this morning. The sun was shining through the curtains in her small room. She decided she'd have a bath, then take Judy for a walk. She must make the most of the sunshine while it lasted; the light was getting lazy, the shade longer, the warmth deceptive as summer ebbed. Suddenly she heard Nellie calling.

"Margery, Margery. Are you awake?"

What could it be? Nellie knew she was not on duty this morning but she could hear her coming down the hallway, treading heavily and wheezing.

"Look, girl. Look what's come." Nellie poked her head round the bedroom door, holding out a small card, thrusting it at her as if it were a delicacy. It was pre-printed, like the Field Service postcard she'd received when Brian was deployed. But this one was different; it was new and it had Brian's writing on it. To Margery that meant everything. What did it say? The title line read:

Camp for prisoners of war.

So that was it – he was a prisoner. Her heart thumped and her head spun; he was alive. He had filled in the date on the card.

14th June 1940.

There it was, in his own writing. Ten weeks ago. Why did it take so long for news to come through?

'I am in German captivity and am quite allright.'

There was an option to say *'slightly wounded'* but she noticed that he had crossed it out. She was glad; she had been thinking he might be like her patients – or worse.

'I shall be transferred from here to a permanent camp and will send you the new address later.'

She thought he would probably have got there by now – wherever it was. But no address had come through yet.

'There I shall be allowed to write again and to receive your mail.'

Margery wept. At last, at last, she had news, the news she'd been waiting for. Nellie sat down beside her on the bed and put her arm round Margery's shoulders.

"You'd better come and have a nice cup of tea."

"He's all right Mum. A prisoner but all right."

"I know, Bert told me and I read it."

Margery realised that the whole village would know the contents of her postcard. That was how it was in small communities; Bert, the Vicar, Alf from next door, Mr Cheeseman at the garage, they all knew Brian and they would all rejoice.

Although she had no address, she would write straight away, a few lines every day, telling him her news, her thoughts, her feelings. It would be like a diary of her wartime life and she could send it when his address came through. She would start with Doris's visit, news about little John and Joey. Those were joys they could share, this web of families and memories. He'd be pleased she was getting on so well with his sister.

But she wouldn't be able to tell him about the German plane; that would never get through the censor. She wondered whether her letters would be limited, only so many per month perhaps? These were details she had yet to learn but they didn't matter. The important point was that he was still alive and would come home – when the war ended.

England, September 1940

Fleda fitted in at Stone Cottage like a piece in a jigsaw. She was an older sister to Margery, a daughter to Nellie and her flippant sense of humour cheered them both up. On the Sunday when Peter came to lunch, she was there laying the table and handing round drinks while Margery and Peter sat on the sofa and chatted. Nellie carved the chicken, one of their old hens gone past her laying days, and she placed the cabbage and roast potatoes on the oak table by the door in the sitting room. The light was dim at that end of the room as the window was small. Peter, Margery, Nellie and Fleda took their places round the table.

"That's top notch, Mrs Street," said Peter. "It's the best spread I've had since the war started."

"Nellie can conjure a feast from a wilderness," said Fleda. "Like loaves and fishes." Margery laughed but she noticed that Peter looked askance; he was religious and wasn't used to Fleda's irreverence.

"We're lucky to have a big garden," said Nellie. "And good neighbours to help us with the digging. Bert turns the ground over and digs in plenty of horse manure, then Margery can manage the rest."

Margery smiled; she had begun to enjoy gardening,

planting tiny seeds in the warm soil, weeding and watering them in the cool of the evening, tending the seedlings till they grew into plants, big strong plants that produced vegetables. It was satisfying and it certainly helped to eke out their rations.

"That must keep you pretty busy, when you're not at work," said Peter, looking across the table at Margery.

"G…g…gardening, helping M...m...mum with the shopping, looking after Joey and Judy – I am pretty b…b…busy as you say." Margery was hesitant with Peter in her own home and it brought her stammer back. She liked him but she didn't want to give him the wrong impression. She was engaged to Brian, after all.

"Shopping's quite a task now," said Nellie. "So many things are hard to get even if they're not rationed. I haven't seen a banana for months."

"But the worst thing," said Fleda, "is the washing. I can't find anyone to wash my smalls. Even Phyllis has gone now, into the Land Army." Margery noticed Peter's expression as Fleda mentioned her smalls at the table.

"What's the Land Army?" Peter turned the conversation to safer ground.

"A load of young girls dressed up in green jumpers and jodhpurs. They help farmers, market gardeners and so on."

"My friend Phyllis has joined up. She's g…g...gone to work on a chicken farm and she's very proud of her uniform."

"Now, girl, you and Peter go and get Joey ready for your drive," said Nellie. "Fleda and I can do the dishes."

"But don't you want to come with us, Fleda?"

"No, Margery, not today. I think I'll just stay here and

have a quiet doze."

So Margery harnessed Joey to the trap and took Peter for a drive *à deux* on the Surrey heathland. It was at its best in the autumn sunshine, the slanting light lingering over the silver birches and the purple heather; the gorse was in flower and Margery noticed a few bees foraging.

"There's been a good crop of late honey," she said. "Alf, our next door neighbour, keeps bees and he's promised Mum a few jars in exchange for eggs."

"She seems to do pretty well with her bartering," said Peter. "It's lovely on this heathland, really grand country but it's very different from home."

"Tell me about South Africa. Brian talks about going there after the war." Margery brought Brian into the conversation to remind Peter of his existence and her status as an engaged woman; she didn't want any misunderstandings.

"Well, Margery, it's veldt land, with brown grasses as far as you can see. The sky seems big, much bigger than here, as it's very flat so you can see for miles in every direction. There's no trees to speak of, only a bit of scrub; nothing like this." He waved his hand at the birch trees and the pines forming a small wood away to their left. "It's all so dry, you see."

It sounded an alien landscape, very different from England. Margery found it hard to imagine brown grass. She wondered about the wide-open skies and the heat. She thought it might be interesting to see South Africa, with Brian of course. Then Peter talked about the people, the Negroes. Margery had never seen a black person. She was curious but it all sounded very strange; she didn't think she'd want to settle there.

"I'd love it if you came to South Africa, Margery. My family are dying to meet you. I've told them so much about you."

Margery felt uncertain. She was used to a small social circle; the boys with whom she had danced, gone to the flicks, played tennis were the sons of Nellie's friends, the brothers of her schoolmates, or one of Johnnie's chums. She knew their families, their schools, their homes and that web of relationships formed a cocoon, a protective bubble. But she didn't know Peter's family. What had he told them about her? She knew he had a promising future as a doctor and he was fun to be with, but he wasn't Brian. She longed for him, his familiar touch, the tickle of his moustache, the feeling that she was safe with him. Her heart ached for him, but he wasn't there.

England, December 1940

Margery heard the telephone ring as she washed the cabbage for lunch. She dried her hands on her apron and went into the hall to answer it. A cold draught was blowing under the front door and racing along towards the bathroom. I hope it's a quick call; this hall is a wind tunnel. I must get that old rug out and lay it along the bottom of the door.

"Brookwood 2323."

"Hello, Curly. How's tricks?"

"Hello Johnnie, we're expecting you for lunch. Is everything all right?"

"Yes, fine old girl. I'm just ringing to let you know I'm bringing a chum too. Andrew he's called. He'll keep you company while I'm busy with Norah. Let Mum know, will you?"

"Of course. See you later, Johnnie." Shivering, Margery went back into the kitchen where the oven warmed the small space; she told her mother about their unexpected guest.

"We'd better do a few more potatoes and some carrots as well. Then if I slice the meat thinly, it should go round nicely." Nellie loved it when her children brought their friends home and filled her cottage with their lively babble. She would find enough food, despite rationing,

"I wonder what this Andrew is like."

"We'll soon see, Mum. They'll be here in about an hour. Better get a move on with dinner."

"We can always have a second glass of sherry if I'm a bit behindhand." Nellie lit another cigarette and put the potatoes round the meat.

When Johnnie brought Andrew into the kitchen, Nellie, Margery and Norah had the dinner under control. Nellie shooed the young people – and their sherry – into the front room by the fire while she made the gravy. Johnnie and Norah snuggled close together on the sofa while Margery and Andrew took the two armchairs by the French doors. The table was laid at the other end of the room.

"I hear you're engaged, Margery," said Andrew. Margery noticed his kind brown eyes in his cheerful face. He listened as if he was really interested in what she had to say. Johnnie never listened; he liked to dominate the conversation.

"Yes, I am. We should have been married by now but Brian got captured in France."

"Yes, Johnnie told me about that. I am sorry. It was a bad show, Dunkirk. I'm rather glad we missed that one. But tell me, can you write to him?"

"Oh, yes, I've started getting letters through now he's in a proper camp. Oflag VIIC it's called."

"I think they sent them all there, all the officers they captured at Dunkirk. I've got a friend there. It must be getting pretty crowded, I should think."

"Oh Curly." Johnnie detached himself from Norah. "While I remember it. Could you ask Bri whether he knows what's happened to old Nick Robbins? No-one's heard from him yet."

"You mean Nick who you were at school with? The boy with the big teeth?"

"That's the one. But he did grow into his teeth as he got older." They all laughed as Nellie came in with the meat and started to carve. Margery thought back to those wretched days before she had heard from Brian; the uncertainty had gnawed at her like toothache, sore and tender, never giving her any peace. How wretched it must be for Nick's family. It was better to know, whatever that meant, than not to know. She thought of Brian's letters, his precious letters, telling her how much he loved her, offering to free her from her engagement if that was what she wanted. She didn't, emphatically not; she'd told him so.

"So what's the news from old Bri?" asked Johnnie as they all sat round the table.

"Well, he reads a lot of books and he's getting quite a dab hand at cooking."

"That's handy because you don't even know how to boil an egg, do you Curly?" Margery decided to ignore that remark.

"He's also playing bridge regularly."

"I bet he'll be quite the card sharper when he gets home. He'll be so good that he'll beat the lot of us," said Nellie, who had always been fond of her cards. "Do you play bridge, Andrew?"

"No, I'm afraid not."

"Never mind, old chap," said Johnnie. "How about coming over one weekend and we four could go to a dance at the Pantiles. Bri won't mind, will he Curly?"

"No, Johnnie, he wants me to go out and have fun. It'll be grand. Something interesting to tell him about in my letters."

England, March 1941

As Nellie drove into the gravel drive at Ditham Croft, Margery noticed that Brian's little car wasn't there. It had stood in the corner under the big oak tree since he left, its presence promising his return; but now it had gone. Frank came out to greet them.

"Hello Mrs Street. Hello Margery, my dear," he said, kissing her cheek.

"Hello Dad." Margery had no problem calling Frank Dad; her own father had died when she was just a child. Her mother went ahead to greet Amy and Margery touched Frank's arm.

"I was wondering what has happened to Brian's car?"

"Amy found it distressing, the car being here when Brian's not, so she got rid of it. We've put the money in the bank for him, of course."

"Oh!" Margery knew it was hard for Amy; she had devoted her life to her children and three of them had still been living at home when the war started. Now they had all left. All the same, selling his car felt like a betrayal, as if Amy didn't think Brian would come back. Margery had read about the mass murders in the Baltic States, thousands of prisoners marched out into the forests and shot. These reports haunted her, day and night, but she had to hang on to her lifeline. He would come home; she was certain he would. If she said it often enough it had to be true.

She went into the house and Amy wheeled the tea trolley into the drawing room, where they sat on hard chairs round a small fire. There was a cup of weak tea without sugar and one shortbread finger for each of them. Brian's letters to his parents were on the low table and Margery reached into her bag for hers. She had many more than they had, but she was his fiancée, after all. Amy sniffed and pursed her lips as she saw the size of Margery's bundle. The room felt chilly, the tea tepid, the chairs stiff as Margery opened the first letter.

Kriegsgefangenenpost, it said at the top, prisoner of war post.

"He says he's only allowed to send two cards and two letters each month," she said. "So if I tell you my news and you tell me yours, he won't have to repeat things."

Margery knew there were passages in his letters that were for her eyes alone, too personal, too private to be shared; his expressions of love, his hopes for their shared future, she wouldn't read those out. She would stick to safe topics like mountain views, the weather and his camp routine. Perhaps she'd better not mention that he was playing bridge; she knew Amy frowned on card games.

Doris came in with little John in his school uniform and

the mood in the room lightened. She had the knack of handling Amy and smoothing things over with her easy chatter. The fire burned brighter, the chairs felt softer, the shortbread tasted sweeter with Doris around.

"Margery, it's so good to see you."

"Hello Doris. Hello, John. I think you've grown since I saw you at Christmas."

"Yes, I have. I had my birthday last week and Daddy measured me. I've grown a whole inch since last birthday. I'm seven now."

Doris went off to help Amy fetch more tea, leaving John babbling happily to Margery about school and football.

"John, have you washed your hands?" said his grandmother as she put down a glass of milk and a shortbread finger for him. John went off to comply and Doris claimed Margery's attention.

"Are these Brian's letters? My little brother is becoming quite a correspondent, isn't he?" With Doris to mediate, Margery told her news and the tea party settled into a comfortable rhythm.

"Have you been shopping, Margery?" Doris asked.

"Yes, and I've been really lucky. You know that shoe shop round the back in Slough? Not the one in the High Street, the other one. Well, they had a pair of black shoes, flat black shoes for work. And guess what? They actually had my size."

"What a treat. You must be so pleased. You really need a comfy pair of shoes, don't you?"

"They make such a difference when I'm on my feet the whole time at the hospital."

"I expect you find the work tiring, my dear." Amy made

it sound as if Margery were a frail invalid instead of a well-built healthy young woman.

"It is tiring, that's true but I enjoy it. The patients are interesting and I'm learning a lot. I always wanted to be a nurse."

"I never worked, of course. My parents could afford to support me, but I suppose it helps to pass the time," Amy said with a sniff. Dad's lovely, Margery thought; it's Brian's mother I find so difficult. She seems to disapprove of everything, including me. I know Brian would like us to get to know each other; but it's difficult.

CHAPTER 18

Laufen, September 1940

When Brian saw the Red Cross trucks drive through the camp gates he was delighted; he had been waiting for this, they all had. He turned up his collar as the wind blew down from the mountains, icy cold; it pierced through his battledress and he shivered. His mouth felt gritty from acorn coffee, the texture reminding him of a muddy puddle. There would be nothing more until the midday soup arrived, thin and watery with a slice of black bread as hard as cardboard. The Goon rations kept them going, just about, but the arrival of the Red Cross parcels was a big event.

"They've come in the nick of time," said Bob. "My clothes don't fit as I've lost so much weight." Brian knew that Bob's ribs were sticking out and his face looked hollow, too much skin and not enough flesh under the thick dark hair that was growing back.

"Yes, it would have been hard facing winter with only Goon food." Brian dreamed about his first parcel, savouring it, relishing it, like one of the five Fry's boys and he planned to make the food last until the next one arrived: it was one a fortnight, that was the rule.

He went to the parcels office and gave his name and number. The Goon on duty scanned his list and checked Brian off. Then he started unpacking Brian's parcel, opening the tins, unwrapping the packages, tipping everything into one container, sardines, plums and dried fruit all muddled together.

"Hey, what are you doing?" The Goon continued,

zombie-like, while Brian hopped from leg to leg in frustration.

"They're inspecting it," said John. "They're worried about what might be hidden in there – guns, knives, that sort of thing. Just what you'd expect in tinned sardines, eh?"

"But once it's opened, I'll have to eat everything at once."

"Yes, it's a bad show."

"That's the last straw." Brian took the contents back to his room. He'd been counting on the parcel but if he couldn't store the food… then what?

"Bob, would you like to share this stuff with me? I can't eat it all before it goes mouldy."

"Thanks, Brian, and then we'll share mine." They ate like kings for a couple of days, but one night they both had to run for the latrines, retching and straining.

"It must have been that salmon," said Bob, wiping his face. "It did smell a bit high."

"We'll have to chuck the rest." Brian knew that they could ill-afford to waste food; under-nourishment weakened their strength, their health and their very chances of survival. The officers looked like coat hangers when they took their shirts off; they had no flesh to keep them warm as winter pressed down from the Bavarian mountains. Brian kept thinking about the dilemma, returning to the issue like a terrier with a rabbit.

"You know, Bob, if six of us got together and shared our parcels, we could draw one every couple of days. That would mean we could use everything before it went off."

"Mmm. You mean we'd live communally?"

"Yes, that's the idea. We could form a mess group and

take turns with the cooking. What do you think?"

"Sounds good me," said Bob. "But we need to be careful who we work with. There are all sorts in here, some good eggs and some rotters."

"That's very true." Brian rubbed his chin, remembering how one of his brother officers had tried to diddle him out of his share of bread; you had to watch carefully as he cut the slices.

"Well now, Tom's a good lad and Pop might come in too."

"And Bill, and what do you think about Allan?"

"That'd be fine."

Brian liked cooking; it gave him something to focus on, something he *had* to do. He hadn't liked his job in the bank but at least it had structured his day; with nothing to do, time hung on his hands. Cooking was a novelty. It had been women's work at Ditham Croft but now he enjoyed devising meals from their random ingredients; it was like solving a riddle or a jigsaw puzzle. He remembered the time he and Margery went to the circus and bought coffee and cake from a stall. The lad had turned to Brian and said: "You know what, guv? I'll make someone a good wife one day." Brian and Margery had grinned at the implied switch in gender roles; but now he could say the same thing. He must remind Margery of that incident when he next wrote; these memories brought her close to him.

Brian felt civilised eating with his mess mates and exchanging news. It felt like mealtimes at Ditham Croft, but decidedly less formal. He began to settle in and get the hang of life in Laufen.

Brian woke up reluctantly; it was his birthday, his twenty-fourth birthday. He lay on his bunk and thought back to last year when he had celebrated at Newbury with Simon and the other officers; that had been a memorable night. What a lot had happened since then. His engagement, those happy days with Margery, their battle and capture; that was four months and two days ago. Dark clouds pressed in, stifling him. He was on an emotional roller-coaster and this was a down day.

He tried to look ahead but the future seemed hidden. Oflag VIIC was a limbo-land between his before-the-war past and his after-the-war future. How long would the war last? Which side would emerge victorious? Would Margery wait for him? His future depended on these imponderables; it was a crossword puzzle with too many difficult clues.

He knew he couldn't expect the usual birthday cards, presents, or letters. He hadn't heard from Margery for five months and had nothing tangible to remember her by as her photograph, her letter and his little mementos had all gone up in flames in 'the Keep'. He ached for her, a deep yearning in his chest, in the pit of his stomach. He longed for a letter, her letter, but no letter came.

I must put a brave face on it, he thought. They'd all want to wish me well – Margery, Johnnie, Doris, Mum and Dad – but they can't so I'd better do it for them. Happy Birthday, Brian, he said to himself; he felt like a child with only imaginary friends.

"You're looking a bit down in the mouth today," said Bob. Brian hesitated and then decided to spill the beans. After all, a trouble shared was a trouble halved as his father always used to say.

"You see, it's my birthday, Bob, and tomorrow's my father's birthday. We always used to celebrate together, the oldest and the youngest members of the family. Mum would bake a cake and everyone would gather around, presents, candles and singing. But this year we can't." He paused and sighed before adding: "I feel a bit browned off."

"That's hard." Bob's forehead puckered with concern for his friend. "I tell you what we'll do: I drew a parcel yesterday, so there's lots of stuff on the shelf. Let's try and concoct a special dinner together. We'll be duty cooks and it might be amusing. I'll see if I can scrounge a bottle of wine from someone or other and we'll have a little celebration in our mess group." Bob's thoughtfulness was a lantern scattering the darkness.

"Thanks, Bob. That's kind. It's a great idea."

Laufen, November 1940

The frost crusted Brian's blanket in the morning; it glittered on the lime trees, painted patterns on the windows and turned Brian's breath to steam. His muscles tensed, stiff with the cold; he still had only his battledress to wear, the battledress in which he'd been captured. One morning the Goons came into his room with a consignment of greatcoats for the *Kriegies*. Brian fingered the thick cloth; that's wool, he thought, that'll help to keep me warm.

"You look a proper swell," said Brian to Bob as they tried on the coats. They felt cosy but the coats were peacock blue.

"I could say the same about you. I hear the Goons took them from the Dutch Army when they surrendered."

"Dead men's clothes? Anyway, it's just the job. I lost my greatcoat in the fire." Brian wore his gaudy coat day and night, indoors and outdoors; he was never without it, as winter rolled down from the mountains.

One morning a Goon walked into their room bearing a bundle of letters. He threw them onto the table and the officers jumped from their bunks and rushed forward, elbowing each other out of the way. It was the first post the *Kriegies* had received since they arrived.

"Let me see."

"Is there one for me?"

Charles, the senior officer, took charge. He collected the pile of mail, turned each envelope over and read out the names one by one.

"Captain Powell. Captain Smith."

The tension in the room was palpable as each recipient took his post and sought privacy; but the room afforded none. They lay on their bunks, huddled in corridors, sat on the stone staircase or stood with their face to the wall while they read their letters.

"Captain King. Captain Watkins."

Letters came from wives, sweethearts, fiancées, friends or parents, bearing good news, bad news or simply news. It was their first contact with the world 'back there', the world they'd lived in before the war. The air crackled with emotion. The rest of the officers waited; Brian felt as if all the leaves from the lime tree were rustling, scrunching, churning in his stomach.

"Captain Dowling," said Charles.

Brian's head felt dizzy and his fingers fumbled as he reached for the envelope. Black spots danced in front of his eyes as he made his way to his bunk. He turned his face to the wall and looked at the envelope – yes, yes, it was from Margery. He trembled with emotion at the sight of her writing, at the knowledge that she had touched this envelope, had licked the stamp. Just holding the letter was enough. He put it to his lips and a thrill shook his body. Slowly, carefully he opened the envelope, savouring every moment. It was dated 3rd September, over two months ago. Trembling, he read the opening lines – and wept with relief. All at once the room seemed brighter, the atmosphere cosier, his roommates friendlier than before. She loved him still. He needed no more.

Laufen, December 1940

Brian felt better once the post came through; letters brought news, gossip, dialogue. He asked questions and Margery replied; she sent him books and they discussed them. He outlined his daily routine and she told him stories from the hospital. They were talking to each other again, they could dream together about the things they would do after the war, simple things like picking primroses, driving Joey, going for a picnic. Although he missed her more than words could tell, life in the camp became… bearable. Parcels came too, bringing cigarettes, food and clothes, much needed clothes.

"You know what, Bob, it's seven months and one day since I last slept in pyjamas. I've been counting." That had been in Wahagnies, in that room he'd shared with Simon; he could have done with Simon's good humour in here. Now he had received a clothes parcel from his family and was beginning to feel comfortable again, a change of underwear, pyjamas, an extra sweater and gloves. Margery knitted him a pair of woollen socks; when he put them on, he glowed all over, knowing her hands had touched the wool, had knitted each sock, had sewed them up and sent them to him.

Margery wrote asking about Nick, Johnnie's friend; his family hadn't heard from him since May. Brian realised that these folks didn't know what had happened. Brian wondered about Martin's sweetheart, about Simon's wife, about Heyworth's family. Would they have been told? Brian knew the story about Nick. His mates said he had been sent out on patrol but hadn't come back; they feared the worst. His fate was lost, buried like a single pebble on a beach.

Christmas came – and went. Brian's mess group did their best to celebrate with a pudding made from dried fruit in the Red Cross parcels, and a bit extra for dinner. It couldn't compare to the previous year when he had proposed to Margery on Boxing Day, but he put a brave face on it. The theatre group staged a pantomime and that was better than nothing. Brian and Bob bought their tickets for *McLaddin and his Wonderful Lighter* and took their seats. They enjoyed the pantomime dame, the corps de ballet – *Kriegies* in tutus – and all the traditions of this very British ritual.

Laufen, February 1941

"Have you seen the ice?" Bob said. The parade ground had frozen over. Snow glinted on the trees, covering the twigs and the wire with sparkling fur. The *Kriegies* used the parade ground as an ice rink.

"I love skating," said Brian. He glided across the ice, sliding, swooping, flying; he wished he could fly over the wire and away, far away... to Margery. Was it freezing in England too, he wondered? All day long Brian and Bob muffled themselves up against the glittering cold and skated; it was good exercise.

The *Kriegies* arranged an ice hockey tournament. The players scuttled this way and that, intent on scoring the winning goal while the spectators stamped their feet and blew on their fingers.

"I bet you five fags the green team wins," said Brian.

"You're on," said Bob. The *Kriegies* loved a little flutter; it made the match more interesting. All too soon the castle loomed dark above them. The light was fading, the sun tinting the snow rosy pink as it dropped behind the mountains.

"We'd better go in now for our bridge tournament." Brian was playing bridge regularly in the evenings and was becoming an experienced player. Bob bent to take off his skates.

"Bridge certainly helps to pass the time."

"I feel we're just waiting for the end of the war but, much as I want to get back to Margery, I don't really want it to end yet, not with all these Jerry gains."

"No, old chap. The way things are going, an armistice wouldn't really settle anything, would it?"

"I don't think Winnie's even thinking of giving up, thank goodness. We'd better keep our chins up for a bit longer, Bob."

"And who knows? We might be good enough to be professional bridge players by the time the war ends."

"That's my career sorted then." Brian smiled as he thought of his parents' reaction. His mother would sniff and ask what the neighbours would say while his father would mention prospects and pensions. Their world – the world where social appearances mattered – seemed a long way from this dirty overcrowded room in a dilapidated palace in the middle of a Bavarian winter. They sat at the table with Tom and Allan and cut for dealer. Brian turned over his cards and looked at his hand.

"Two no trumps." Bob stroked his chin, as he hunched his tall frame over his cards.

Laufen, Spring 1941

Once a week, Brian played bridge with his chums from the Bucks Battalion; they were good players and he enjoyed partnering Bill or John. Bill was rash, taking risks with his bidding, resulting in impossible contracts; John was cautious and they missed contracts they could have made. These men felt like old friends; they came from the same part of the world, had trained with him as weekend soldiers and had been with him at Hazebrouck. Their shared past bound them together.

"Did you hear that the Goons shot a chap the other evening when he was adjusting the blackout blind?" said John.

"I didn't hear about that," said Brian. "But they are trigger happy and they have fired randomly into our room when they see anyone near the windows."

"This was worse than that. They shouted that a light was showing and then fired when the chap adjusted the blind. It was deliberate."

“That’s dreadful. Totally against the Geneva Convention.”

“Elliot says that the SBO has put in a complaint to the Camp Commandant.”

“Quite right too.” Brian lit another cigarette.

“It looks as if this must be the last of our bridge evenings,” said Bill. Brian looked up surprised.

“Oh really? Why is that? Is my play so bad?”

“It’s not that, Brian. John and I are being moved to another camp.”

“That’s news to me.” Brian was astonished. To date, the only *Kriegies* who had left Laufen had been Rupert and his fellow escapees. They had been recaptured and sent to Colditz Castle, the camp for ‘bad boys’. *Kriegies* kept crowding in but no-one ever went out.

“Elliot says the Red Cross has been complaining that Laufen’s overcrowded, long queues for the facilities, not enough recreation space and so on.” Elliot was on the camp committee and in the know about camp administration. “So the Goons are sending some of us junior officers to another camp, in Poland I believe. When we’re gone, you’ll have space for a library, a chapel and a room for the concert party to rehearse.”

“I’ll have to put a brave face on losing my bridge partner then. It must be exciting for you, going out of here, travelling to Poland, seeing another country.”

“Maybe,” said John. “But we don’t know what it’ll be like where we’re going.”

“Nine months in one place gets pretty damned boring,” said Bill. “I’ll be glad of a change.” Brian said goodbye to his friends and hoped that they’d meet again – in happier times.

After Bill and John left, Brian and Bob were moved into a smaller room, one with only 20 inmates; it seemed restful by comparison. Their window looked out onto the small provincial town where the narrow street sloped down to the river. They could see two grocers' shops, a butcher, a newsagent, and a photography studio. Brian thought it looked like the High Street in Slough and he watched women with shopping baskets, children with satchels, and old men with briefcases. Brian was intrigued by this vignette of civilian life in wartime Germany.

"They look just like us, Bob, don't they? Have you noticed that lady over there? A *gnädige Frau* I suppose you'd call her." Brian was going to German classes. "She looks like our next door neighbour in Slough."

"Yes," said Bob. "And there's an old man who walks down each day with a pipe in his mouth to buy a newspaper; he looks like my father."

"That young woman is about the same age as Margery."

"I've noticed her every morning, out shopping for bread and groceries."

"It's funny to see them," said Brian. "They're going about their ordinary business, whereas in here nothing feels ordinary; we could be… in different worlds. But they're just outside the glass."

The snow on the mountains began to melt and the river rushed, in full flood, below the castle. Then the sticky buds on the chestnut trees burst and the leaves unfurled like fingers. May brought the first anniversary of Brian's capture and Elliot organised a dinner party for the Bucks Battalion. Brian recalled their defence of Hazebrouck, the bravery of his men, the fall of 'the Keep' and their surrender; he relived those few days, every scene intense, vibrant, distinct. They stood out in sharp relief, like his enchanted interlude with Margery, the best and the worst moments of his life.

"The Goons are going to organise a photo session," Elliot told him at the dinner. "The town photographer is coming to take pictures of us, alone and in groups. Then you can order copies to send to friends and family at home."

"That's a grand idea," said Brian.

"It's a good propaganda exercise too. Photos of us *Kriegies* will show the world that they are treating us properly."

"There's many a lie told by the camera. Without the Red Cross parcels, we'd have looked pretty wretched by now."

"Yes, but we need to think about morale back at home. It'll give our folks a boost. If they can see we're all right, they'll feel better about the war." Brian knew that British troops were fighting in North Africa, and that Italy had joined Hitler who was still allied to Soviet Russia. The United States remained studiously neutral. The progress of the war was dismal.

"I see what you mean. Margery will be pleased to have a picture of me and I'd like to get one of our mess group too." Brian remembered that Elliot had helped to organise the camp library.

"The library's really good, Elliot. I'm using it regularly. I enjoy reading but I never had time before the war. I'm a slow reader, you see, but now time's no problem. I've just started on the Classics, Dickens and Jane Austen and I've read modern novels like *Rebecca* and *All This and Heaven Too*."

"*Rebecca*'s a lovely book," said Elliot.

"Yes, I want to go to Cornwall with Margery, for our honeymoon perhaps, and find a little place like Du Maurier's happy valley." This was added to Brian's list of things they would do together after the war.

Laufen, August 1941

A rumour drifted through the camp, like soft summer mist. No-one knew who started it, nobody knew whether it was true but it gathered strength and spread until everyone was wrapped in its gentle folds. Brian thought it was like Santa Claus, such a seductive idea that you wanted to believe it. He had been crowded with the other *Kriegies* in Laufen Castle, like chickens in a coop for 16 months. Moving camp was an exciting prospect. Brian looked forward to a different view; mountains were beautiful but teasing, tantalising if you could only look. He and Bob were like schoolboys at the end of term, demob-happy.

But then the mist changed; it became a cold choking cloud, with fear swirling in its midst. Laufen was grim but the *Kriegies* had got used to it. Brian had made friends with Bob, Allan and the others; he had got the measure of the guards, learning which of them could be bribed to bring in an extra blanket, a pack of cards, a bottle of wine. If they moved, they'd leave all that behind. Brian clung to what he knew.

The weeks of rumour and counter rumour continued throughout September and Brian's birthday, his second in captivity, came and went at Laufen. When would they go? Where would they go? What could they take with them?

Innumerable questions bubbled in the air.

In early October, they were told to be ready to leave in three days' time. How could he decide which items to take and which to leave? What would the new camp be like? They said that conditions would be worse than here – no brick buildings, no exercise area, no electric light. With only two days to go they felt at home in Laufen; they knew the rules, knew how to survive. Elliot said they must march out of Laufen with their heads held high; they'd show the Goons that British officers were unbowed by captivity. But, for all that, going to a new camp seemed like stepping off the edge of a cliff.

Wales and Germany, 2016

"We can get a plane from Cardiff, Mum, and take the train to Laufen," said Amy. "It's easy to get there."

It was my 70th birthday present, a trip to Laufen Castle, where my father had been interned as a prisoner-of-war. Our trip was straightforward, his was arduous. He completed his journey by rail, not in a comfortable carriage like us, but herded into a cattle wagon. He took ten days to arrive; we took a few hours.

From the station to the castle, we walked downhill; the streets were empty as we splashed through the rain in our waterproofs. He wore his uniform, the clothes he was wearing when he was captured; he had nothing else.

"Do you think Grandad came this way?" Amy asked.

"I'm sure he did." The townspeople, the Germans, the enemy, had lined the road to watch him march by, a dirty, disheveled prisoner in British Army uniform. It was like a

Roman triumph, the captives paraded, humiliated by their conquerors.

As we approached the castle, I noticed the chestnut trees, flaunting their white candles, their finger-shaped leaves dripping onto the pavement. Their flowers would have dropped when he arrived, a white carpet covering the street like snow.

I stood in front of the building and looked up. So this was it; a once dilapidated palace now refurbished to provide comfortable, modern apartments for middle class, provincial Germans. Standing bleakly against the grey skies was the watchtower by the gateway. He called it 'the entrance' because no-one went out. He was here for sixteen months, a rabbit in a cage, never allowed to leave, never to wander in the woods and mountains beyond the wire.

He ate cabbage soup and stale black bread, a miserable diet for a hungry young man. We noticed a Pizza Parlour in the castle and sought refuge, our coats dripping like tears.

"Do you think Grandad was here?" Amy said. "In this very room?"

"I don't know. I suppose he might have been. They had social areas on the ground floor – the library, the theatre, the chapel. One of them might have been here."

When we had eaten our meal, I pulled two photographs from my bag. They had been taken in Laufen during the war and sent to my mother. The first was a picture of a smart young man in Army uniform, chest thrust forwards, hands behind his back, gazing directly at the camera. Behind him was a stone staircase with an iron handrail. This photo had sat in a silver frame in my parents' sitting room throughout their married life. The second was a group photo, him and his mess mates. The six young men stood together, smiling in the shade of a lime tree.

"I'll ask the waitress if she knows where these were taken. There's no point just wandering around in the rain." In my halting German, I asked the waitress about the staircase and the lime tree. I pointed to the thin young man in the photo.

"Er ist mein Vater. Er war hier im Krieg." I said. "He is my father. He was here in the war."

She turned the photo over in her hand and looked at the postmark. 1941, it said, and she put her hand up to her mouth. The war was far distant from her young life; she had been born in a reunified Germany at the heart of the European Union. Did she know Laufen Castle had once been a prisoner-of-war camp? She took the photo to her colleague and they whispered warily to each other, like friends with a guilty secret. Then they directed us to a narrow lane that led downwards to a strip of land on the riverbank. And there they were: the stone staircase, the iron handrail and the lime tree. I touched the rail, the metal cold under my fingers and I stood on the very spot where his picture had been taken; I trembled.

I looked across the river to the woods and mountains rising steeply beyond the town. He must have become familiar with this view and I remembered how he had described it to my mother, his fiancée.

'The fresh greens of the trees, the darkness of the firs, the bloom of the fruit trees and chestnuts and always the changing mysteries of the mountains.' The words of the young lover spilled off the page like poetry. With his wedding postponed, his dreams in tatters, he sustained his

love through Red Cross airmail letters, the flimsy paper encompassing his ardour.

He had never come back to Laufen, never revisited this castle where he had passed such a traumatic interlude in his life. After the war, he moved on but he had never forgotten. I remembered his habit of changing his clothes before his evening meal. When he was working, he took off his business suit, and, after he retired, he changed his shirt; it was a ritual. But as he got older, he struggled. Weak with cancer, it was hard to walk to the stairlift, to lift his arms, to change his clothes.

"Don't do it, Dad," I said, one evening. "It's only me and Mum. You're fine as you are." He turned to me, almost fiercely.

"I spent five years of my life in uniform with no other clothes to wear," he said. "I consider it a privilege to be able to change."

My mother lifted her eyebrows and I shrugged my shoulders as I helped him onto the stairlift. I said nothing. I was hesitant to reopen memories of a past he had ceased to talk about years before. It was a missed opportunity; he died a week later.

CHAPTER 19

England, July 1941

"Have you heard the news?" Peggy said, bursting through the cloakroom door. "St Thomas's are leaving. They're going back to London now the Blitz is over." Peggy liked to gossip. Margery had just come in and her gabardine dripped as she looked up, one foot raised, one hand struggling with her galoshes, the other resting on the wall.

"But what about us VADs?" Margery frowned as the galoshes spattered mud on her white apron. She liked the hospital and had expected to be there for the duration, until Brian came back and they got married. But now what?

"Well, we can choose. Either we go to train at St Thomas's in London, or we move to another local hospital, or we stay on here and look after the loonies." Brookwood had been a mental asylum before the war. "I reckon I'll go with them if they'll have me. What about you?"

"Mmm, I'll need to think about that."

The two girls chatted it over as they walked to the ward, their footsteps echoing along the corridors. They set to work tidying the beds, taking temperatures and changing pillowcases. I'll miss the routine here, thought Margery. She worked her way up the ward until she came to a bed with screens around it. The young Army officer had been in theatre when she went off duty yesterday and now his face was ashen, with dark shadows round his eyes and his hands clutched the sheet, clenching and unclenching. She touched his hand; it was furnace hot.

"Nurse, nurse, help me, please help me." He reminded

her of Brian with his fair curls and his moustache. She was supposed to be tidying the beds, but surely he needed more than a straightened sheet. Was this a case for using her initiative? But what would Fanny Curtis say if she called her and it was a false alarm? I know, I'll do his observations and then I'll call Sister if they're out of line. She put the thermometer under his arm and felt for the pulse in his wrist; she noted the readings, then strapped the band around his arm to take his blood pressure. She made up his chart, then left the cubicle, closed the screens and went to Sister's desk.

"What is it?" Sister looked up from her notes and saw Margery standing with her hands behind her back.

"It's that young officer in Bed 14. His temperature is 102° and his pulse racing. I thought you ought to know."

"Thank you, Nurse Street. I'll go and have a look at him."

Later in the morning Sister called Margery to her desk and she felt guilty about the smudge on her apron. Sister stared straight at Margery.

"You did well this morning, Nurse Street. That patient was in a great deal of pain and I'm pleased that you checked his observations before you called me. You have all the makings of a good nurse."

Margery gaped, unable to believe her ears. Everyone knew that Fanny Curtis didn't trust VADs.

"Thank you, Sister," she mumbled, keeping her hands behind her back, her eyes focussed on the desk.

"Have you ever thought of making a career of nursing? You could come with us to St Thomas's."

Margery's eyes shot up; she had never thought about a career. Girls like her didn't; they just got married. Sister's suggestion was a daffodil in the onion bed.

"N..n..o…o, Sister, not really. B..b..but… I'll ask my mother." She felt pleased that Sister thought her good enough to train. She was invited to the party, even if she couldn't go.

"Your mother? Why? You're over 21 aren't you, Nurse? Old enough to make your own decisions, I should think."

Margery hung her head. Nellie didn't like the idea of living alone and Margery enjoyed their easy mother-daughter relationship. Although Margery liked the idea of getting qualified, of being a proper nurse, not just a VAD, the training took three years and married women were barred. Suppose Brian came home suddenly and they got married? She wouldn't want to quit in the middle of her training. What about her animals, Judy and Joey? Nellie might cope with Judy but never with Joey. There were so many problems, so many difficulties if she were to venture into this unknown world. She was faced with another decision and she didn't know what to do.

"Have you heard, Margery?" said Peter, catching up with her as she went for her lunch break. "We're going back to London. It'd be grand if you come too."

Since she had heard that Brian was a prisoner, her relationship with Peter felt different. She still danced with him at hospital socials, went in a party to the flicks, met up on weekends to show him the countryside; this was her girlhood, after all, her time for fun with her friends. But he seemed to be pushing for more than friendship. She kept saying she was engaged to Brian, committed to him, would have been married to him if only… but Peter had never met Brian.

"He's not here and I am," he said. What did that mean? Margery wondered how their relationship would change if she went away from home, away from her family circle. But, if she didn't go, she couldn't train and she'd be transferred to Woking Hospital; that seemed dull. She would write to Brian and ask him what he thought. That was a good idea; he could decide for her.

England, November 1941

The car spluttered and died. Bother, thought Margery, I'll have to get out – and it's hammering down with rain. Woking was too far for Margery to cycle and Brian had offered her his little car but, as Amy had sold it, she had to use Nellie's elderly Ford, a temperamental beast which objected to bad weather. This was the third time it had let her down – and in the blackout too. There was no alternative; she had better start to walk and try to thumb a lift. She was lucky. After about five minutes Mr West from down the road came past; he was on late shift, saw her and picked her up.

"Thank you so much for stopping. The car's conked out again."

"That's no problem, Miss Street. I can easily drop you home."

"I'm sorry I'm dripping all over your seats."

"It's a filthy night, I know." They chatted away amicably and soon they turned into Brentmoor Road and the journey was over.

"Here you are now." Mr West drew up by her gate. Nellie was aghast when Margery walked in with water streaming off her raincoat and running rivers on the floor.

"You look like a drowned rat," said Nellie. "Take your things off, here by the fire. I'll get your dressing gown and some big towels to rub you dry."

Margery's uniform hung above the stove, steaming like paving stones in the sun; her shoes were filled with paper to dry. She sat by the stove rubbing her long hair while Nellie mopped the floor and made a cup of tea. Suddenly the telephone rang.

"You stay there, girl. I'll get it," said Nellie. Margery kept on rubbing. Long hair is such a nuisance; it's hard to keep tidy under my nurses' cap and I keep getting nits. Besides, it takes so long to dry, like that time Andrew ducked me in the swimming pool and it dripped all down my frock during dinner. Perhaps I'd better have it cut and try one of these new styles. But what would Brian think? He always loved my long hair. Then Nellie came back, clutching her handkerchief and dabbing her eyes. She sat down heavily and lit a cigarette.

"That was Andrew, ringing from Maidstone. Johnnie's got a bad bout of 'flu from that night exercise last week. He's been taken into hospital. It's so worrying."

Margery knew Nellie got things out of proportion, especially where Johnnie was concerned. She decided to play it down; it was probably nothing more than a bad cold. Johnnie always made such a fuss, ever the attention seeker.

"I'm sure he'll be all right, Mum. Hospital's probably just a precaution to make sure he gets the best attention. We'll ring again tomorrow. He'll be on the mend by then, I'm sure."

But he wasn't; his condition deteriorated, turned to pneumonia, and he was delirious. Nellie and Margery decided to visit Maidstone the next day, Margery's day off.

The familiar smell of antiseptic and floor polish greeted Margery as they entered Johnnie's ward. The nurse in charge directed them to his bed, the one with screens.

"Just five minutes, now," the nurse said. "That'll be quite enough." Johnnie's skin was flushed, his breathing shallow and laboured. Margery felt his pulse and found it racing. He didn't know they were there and was babbling incoherently. This is worse than I expected, she thought. She watched the nurses, noting that the ward was well run, the nurses attentive and the charts well kept. When their time was up, they sat in a café with Andrew.

"They're doing all they can, Mum," said Margery. "There aren't any wonder drugs but good nursing will make all the difference." She spoke more confidently than she felt, as if to reassure a fractious patient.

"Oh, I hope so. I hate leaving my boy like this. Perhaps I should stay." She wrung her hands together and dabbed her eyes.

"Mrs Street," said Andrew. "I'm sure it's best for you to go now. He'll be on the mend in a day or two but, if he isn't, then I could find you a room in a good hotel."

"Well, there's an idea, Mum. Come home now and we'll keep in touch. If he doesn't improve, you can come back for a few days later in the week. That's a much better plan." Margery felt she needed to be decisive as Nellie was teetering, like a fledgling on the edge of a branch.

"He'll get better, Mrs Street," said Andrew. "I'm certain

of it. It might be a blessing in disguise. He'll probably get a home posting after this, while I'm sent off to North Africa – or who knows where – to do who knows what."

This was a clever ploy. Margery knew they were training for a secret mission, all very hush hush, but the idea that Johnnie's illness might keep him away from the danger, away from the fighting, would appeal to Nellie.

"Thank you so much, Andrew," she said when Nellie went to tidy herself. "That was just the thing to say to Mum. She's a bit of a drama queen and she does get in a state, especially about Johnnie."

"It's the least I can do, Margery. You folks have been so kind, inviting me to Stone Cottage, treating me like one of the family. It's been fun and I'm glad to help. I just hope he's going to pull through."

"Yes, it looks like touch and go to me."

Andrew nodded and smiled at her.

"Just beat them up, put them in the pan and stir. Nothing can go wrong with scrambled eggs," said Fleda, cracking eggs and scattering shell all over the kitchen table. Margery wasn't so sure; Fleda was not noted for her culinary skills. It was good of her, though, to come to Stone Cottage while Nellie was away. The Dowlings had invited Margery to stay with them but she preferred to be at home and to keep on working. The supper smelt, a strong whiff of sulphur as Fleda slopped egg on the stove. Clouds of smoke rose from the toast in the grill.

"Just scrape the burnt bits off over the sink, Margery," said Fleda. Margery looked at the sink, full of unwashed bowls and dirty plates, and she began to giggle.

"Hey Fleda, this kitchen looks just like yours."

"It must be catching, like the measles. Just pile the crockery up on the draining board. We'll deal with it tomorrow."

"But tomorrow never comes."

"I know. That's the good thing about it." The telephone shrilled its insistent call from the hall and Margery went to pick up the receiver.

"Brookwood 2323."

"Hello, Margery." It sounded like Brian; her heart leaped and her stomach churned. Had he got home unexpectedly? Was it really him?

"It's Bernard," said the voice. Oh no, not Brian but his brother! Of course, their voices sounded similar on the phone. Margery felt limp, like a flag without wind.

"I'm ringing to find out if there's any news of Johnnie?"

She must pull herself together and be polite.

"So kind of you to ring, Bernard. Yes, he's out of danger. The crisis has passed."

"You must be so pleased. I am glad."

"Thank you. We are, but unfortunately that's not all. The doctors say there's a shadow on his lungs. It's TB."

"I *am* sorry. But I'm told there's lots they can do now if you catch it early. How's he taking it?"

"He doesn't know yet. We're waiting till he's stronger before we tell him." They exchanged family news and then Margery hung up and returned to her supper. It hadn't improved; the toast was soggy, the egg congealed.

"Poor old Johnnie," said Fleda. "This TB will clip his wings a bit." Margery thought of her brother, full of jokes, of crazy pranks; he had such a zest for living. The damage to his lungs might make him a semi-invalid; it seemed cruel, like cutting down the brightest flower in the garden.

"Yes, indeed. He's to go to a sanatorium for a bit to see how he gets on, but he might even be invalided out of the Army altogether." Margery knew Johnnie would hate that. He'd been so proud of his commission, so keen to distinguish himself in action, so jealous of Brian when he went to France.

England, January 1942

"I need a bit of sympathy, Mum." Johnnie was lying on the sofa by the fire, his legs covered with a rug, his hands limp by his sides.

"My poor boy," said Nellie. "Would you like another cup of tea?"

Margery knew this game; it had special rules. Nellie enjoyed cossetting him as much as he relished the attention. There was no doubt he had been ill, very ill, but now he was well on the way to recovery. His eyes taunted, mocked and he was back on form with teasing.

"Poor old Bri. You don't really love him, Curly. You haven't cleaned his photo frame."

Margery picked up the picture of Brian standing by a stone staircase in Laufen. It had arrived just in time for Christmas and she treasured it. He looked well, standing there in his uniform gazing at the camera, but Johnnie was right: the silver frame could do with a bit of polish.

"I've been so busy fetching and carrying for you. But I tell you what, cleaning silver is a job you could do on the sofa. Shall I fetch the things for you?"

"Not just now, old girl. Touché, I think." Johnnie paused and Margery laughed. It was good to have him home. What luck that the TB had not been as bad as they had feared and there was every hope of a complete recovery, the doctors said, so he had been sent home for three months' leave before the Army reassessed his fitness for duty.

"What are you going to wear to that hospital social next week, Curly?"

Margery was looking forward to the dance as Peter would be there, together with some of the old crowd from St Thomas's. It would be good to meet up with those folks again.

"I don't really know. I haven't any coupons so it'll have to be something I've worn before."

"Why don't you give me a fashion parade? Try on a couple of your dresses and do a twirl." That sounded fun so Margery went to look in her wardrobe. She looked out her bridesmaid's dress, a polka dot shirt-waister and a simple blue dress with a V neck and a belted waist. She put on the blue dress; it was very plain but well cut.

"Di di dee da," she said. She swept round the curtain with a flourish and paraded before Johnnie.

"And Miss Street models our new number," he said. "This versatile day dress is just the ticket for tea parties, dances or dinner dates." Nellie wheezed, laughing as Margery mimed dancing with a cushion in place of a partner.

"Actually, Curly, that colour suits you. It could do the job, with a few additions. Have you got anything else?"

"I've got the old polka dot dress or the red dress I wore when I was Betty's bridesmaid, but I've worn that several times before to hospital dances so I'd rather wear something different."

"I think we could jazz this one up a bit. How about using a bit of velvet from these cushions, Mum, to make a trim?"

Margery knew she would never get away with such a request but Johnnie could twist Nellie round his little finger and Margery snipped and stitched as Johnnie directed.

"Bob's your uncle," said Johnnie. "You'll be the Belle of the Ball."

When Margery arrived at the hospital social, Peter was hovering at the door.

"Here you are," he said. "I've saved you a place at our table. Would you like a drink?" Margery was pleased to see him and to catch up with his news. She hadn't abandoned the idea of going to St Thomas's; she'd just shelved it. She had been so busy recently with Johnnie's illness and Nellie's maternal anxiety that she still hadn't come to a final decision. The prospect of training was dangling before her like beads on a baby's pram, out of reach but tempting.

Tables had been placed around the hall, a bare and dusty space that the Woking Hospital Social Committee had decorated with bunting and paperchains left over from Christmas. The band was good and Margery's feet tapped in time to the music. She loved dancing, the beat surging through her body, her feet moving with the rhythm. She danced with Peter, with Robin, with Guy and with Peter again. He was a good dancer, swirling her around as if she were floating, carried on the current. The room heated with the press of bodies and activity so Margery and Peter stepped outside.

"I've something for you, Margery. It was meant to be a Christmas present but, what with Johnnie's troubles and everything, I haven't seen you so now it's a late Christmas present." He passed her a brown paper parcel. Margery unwrapped it and found a box of candied fruits, a large box; it must have come from his family in South Africa. Margery's mouth watered as she saw the juicy fruits glistening with sweetness; treats like this were unobtainable in wartime Britain. She felt uncomfortable about accepting such a lavish gift; it would place her under an obligation and it didn't feel right.

"No, Peter. I can't accept this. It's too much."

"Margery, you must know how much you mean to me. I've never loved anyone as much as I love you."

"Peter, I'm engaged. You know that." Peter had never met Brian and Margery knew that he thought of him as a chimera.

"But I'm here and he isn't." He echoed the same refrain and Margery knew that was true but it wasn't Brian's fault.

"Think Margery, we could have so much fun together, you and me. You're wasting the best years of your life waiting for Brian but he might never come home."

Margery blanched to hear him voice her worst nightmare. She had heard about these wretched camps with bodies piled in heaps like discarded clothes and knew Brian could be in mortal danger every hour, every day; he depended on her. She felt angry with Peter and, in a flash, she knew she'd stay loyal to her Boxing Day promise.

"No, I'm sorry Peter. I like you very much – as a friend; but that's all it can be. I can't accept your present." Margery turned on her heel and walked back into the hall, the tears stinging her eyes. She felt as if she had closed a door behind her; her decision was taken. She wouldn't go to St Thomas's. Woking was all right and there she'd stay for the duration.

England, April 1942

When Easter arrived Johnnie invited Andrew to stay. Three days' leave was not enough to make the trip to his parents in Scotland.

"Do come in Andrew and make yourself at home," said Nellie as Andrew appeared at the kitchen door.

"Good to see you, old chap." Johnnie got up from the table and shook Andrew's hand.

"How are you doing, Johnnie? Are you still shirking? Surely it's about time you joined us again?"

"I'm due to have my medical in the middle of April and then we'll see. But I'm ticking along quite nicely now. Margery and I took Judy for a walk last week and then we borrowed a couple of nags and went riding."

"Good show. It's not the same in the Mess without you."

"A lot quieter, I should think," said Margery. "He's always spouting off about something."

"We go in for heated debate in the Mess," said Andrew. "He's always posing as a serious thinker, the battalion's philosopher." As Margery laughed she noticed that Johnnie was looking out of the window, studying the blossom on the pear tree. Margery knew he liked to direct the conversation, to be the ringmaster.

"Right now, plans," said Johnnie. "Norah's coming over

tomorrow afternoon and I thought we four could go out for a spot of supper before I run her home. On Sunday, I think we must all go to Matins, then lunch and a nice lazy afternoon, in the garden if it's fine. How does that sound, old boy?"

"Top notch."

Margery looked at Andrew and felt a surge of happiness. It was grand when he came over and she could go out with Johnnie and Norah; this was the way it used to be with Brian, four young people enjoying each other's company. She remembered that time when Brian had been driving his little car with Johnnie and Norah in the back seat and Brian had been teaching them the words of a song. They had roared with laughter together. Now the evenings were getting lighter and the days warmer, Margery felt a surge of energy and optimism. Even the war seemed to be going better; maybe it would soon be over and then... She could hardly bear to hope. Her wedding had already been delayed for two years.

"Johnnie, you've forgotten to tell Andrew about Daisy Jones and the girls. They're coming to tea this afternoon," said Nellie.

"Whoops. Yes, old boy. It's an old chum of Mum's – her Mah-jong adversary as a matter of fact – and she's coming over with two of her daughters, Paddy and Kate. No big deal but I'm just putting you in the picture."

Daisy Jones seemed to be visiting a great deal too much for Margery's liking and she always brought Paddy with her. Paddy, with her frivolous frocks, her voluptuous figure, her outrageous opinions, always made Margery feel inadequate. They had known each other forever and it had always been the same story. Paddy was younger than Margery but she was the stronger swimmer, the better tennis player, the faster runner. It rankled; it always had. She knew what it would be like this afternoon.

"Oh Johnnie," Paddy would say batting her eyes at him. "Could I have a bit of sugar in my tea? I know it's rationed and I'm a naughty girl but I have such a sweet tooth" She would lick her lips and Johnnie would lap it up; he was plasticine in her hands.

On Sunday afternoon they dozed in the sun after lunch. The weather was unseasonably warm but no-one complained.

"That was a delicious meal, Mrs Street," said Andrew.

"That bottle of wine you brought us was perfect," said Nellie. "That's what has made me sleepy."

"I thought a good red would be just the ticket. Tell me Margery, what has happened to Fleda? I'd expected to see her this weekend."

"She's gone off to Birmingham to drive a lorry. She had to do something with this new National Service Act and she'd got fed up of hospital work so she bit the bullet, let her house and she's gone off for the duration. I miss her, you know."

"I bet you do. She's a good sort."

Margery felt contented, remembering the fun they'd had yesterday evening. Andrew was excellent company and good for Johnnie too. He listened but held his own opinions and Margery knew Brian would like Andrew; they could all be friends, after the war.

"Come on, folks. Time for action," said Johnnie. He leapt to his feet and tried to pull Andrew up too. "We'll get our uniforms on, Andrew, and give these girls a marching display. It'll be a bit of fun."

"All right. I'll be with you in a tick." Andrew got up and stretched like a cat and went into the house with Johnnie. Margery watched the garden through half-closed eyes. The daffodils were flowering, and the primroses. She noticed an early butterfly and the birds busy in the hedges. It looked as if a blackbird was building its nest in the holly hedge. Johnnie and Andrew came out in their uniforms.

"Now Mum, you're the top brass, reviewing the troops," said Johnnie. "You'd better wear this hat." He grabbed the tea cosy and placed it on her head. Nellie began to laugh; she could never resist Johnnie.

"Curly, you're her sidekick. Sit there and salute us when we salute you."

Andrew and Johnnie went around the side of the house and reappeared marching smartly, swinging their arms in time with their feet. It was almost like a dance, Margery thought, the rhythm, the beat, the teamwork. They went twice around the lawn then stopped in front of Nellie, stamped their feet and saluted. Nellie and Margery saluted and clapped their hands at the performance.

"Your turn now Curly," said Johnnie. "We'll teach you how to do it."

Margery was willing to give it a go so she stood up and listened to their instructions.

"Right leg and left arm. Then left leg and right arm," said Johnnie. Margery started off all right but soon her arms and legs got out of sync. She started to giggle.

"Try it with Andrew. March behind and copy him." That made things worse; it felt like learning a new ballet dance.

"Arms, legs, keep in time with Andrew," said Johnnie.

"I can't do three things at once, Johnnie," she said.

"Give her a rest old boy," said Andrew. "We spent weeks learning to march – and we didn't have the benefit of a glass of wine first."

Margery felt woozy from the wine and she collapsed laughing on the grass. Andrew lay down beside her and they looked up together at the willow tree framing the sky like a curtain. Andrew is so considerate, Margery thought. She hoped he'd go on coming for weekends, lots of weekends, until the war ended.

CHAPTER 20

Warburg, October 1941

The first thing Brian noticed about their new camp was the mud; squelchy, sticky, smelly mud. It got everywhere, on your boots, your coat, your clothes and even into your bed. There was no avoiding it. The parade ground was a swamp as Brian lumbered across to line up for *Appell.* The second thing he noticed about Warburg was the people; RAF and Army personnel were interned together, a super-camp for officers.

"It's good to see you again," said Brian, bumping into John, his erstwhile lieutenant. John had moved from Laufen last spring. "How's life been treating you?"

"A bit of a mixed bag really, Brian. We went off to Poland and were in a couple of camps there. They were less crowded than Laufen and we had room for a theatre, a church and a social area, but they were pretty rundown."

"All the camps seem to be a bit ramshackle," said Brian. "What was the food like?"

"Dreadful. Same old soup and potatoes, *kartoffeln, kartoffeln, kartoffeln*; it seems to be all the Goons eat but at least we were housed in brick buildings."

"Better than these rickety old huts then?"

"They'd hardly pass as garden sheds back home," said John. Brian chuckled, remembering the shed at the end of his parents' garden, that old glory hole for tools, sacks, wood and cardboard where he'd spent many an hour concocting dens, sledges and go-carts from the confused clutter.

"They're on stilts so we can't dig but that'll make them jolly draughty once winter sets in." Brian listened while

John told him about his travels and the sights he had seen.

"There were several other camps nearby and the conditions in some of them were appalling, especially for the Jews."

"The Goons seem to have a hierarchy of camps and, luckily for us, we're near the top. I pity the poor Ruskies next door; they seem to be having a thin time of it." Brian knew that the *Blitzkrieg* technique had been applied on the Eastern Front and thousands of prisoners had been captured. He remembered his first few months in Laufen as he looked through the wire and saw the Russian prisoners, just thin bundles of rags with eyes too big for their faces.

"I saw them fighting each other yesterday for their soup," said John.

"They're desperate. Stalin didn't sign the Geneva Convention so the Goons are treating them as *Untermensch.*"

"No Red Cross parcels for them, then?"

"No." Brian had passed bread and fags through the wire when he could. He'd seen the bodies piled up by the gates each morning and he knew it would get worse as the cold weather set in. He shivered as he remembered how bad it had been when he arrived at Laufen, hungry, humiliated and deeply suspicious of other inmates. He had set himself to bear it, to survive, to get home to Margery but some of the men hadn't been able to stand it; he shuddered, remembering Larry who'd run for the wire, been shot by the Goons and left hanging there for several days as a lesson to the rest of them. Thank God, I got through it, he thought, those first few months were hell.

"I'm going to pop inside now Brian. I promised Tom I'd

help him with some tin-bashing." With a wave of his hand, John left. Tin-bashing was becoming a tradition, like cricket on the village green or pantomimes at Christmas. Old cans, preferably from Klim, the powdered milk, were bashed into useful items such as stoves, plates, or tea pots.

Brian went on alone picking his way around the parade ground. The sewage trenches had overflowed and seeped into the mud. The smell was worse than a cesspit and Brian hated to think about the germs; Margery was always asking about his health. Bob Smith came out of his hut and joined Brian. The two men no longer shared a room; they had been separated in the move. Brian had felt lost at first but he was trying to appreciate the good points: they had more to say to each other when they did meet and, without Bob by his side, he was meeting new people.

"How are you doing, Brian? Have you formed a Mess group yet?"

"Pretty much, I'm lucky that Bill Thomson is still with me and we've managed to get one or two others to join us so… nearly there." He smiled and spread his hands.

"You know I miss the mountains." Bob peered into the distance beyond the wire, where the grey clouds scudded across the wide open sky.

"I agree," said Brian. "I loved the way they changed with the seasons. The chestnut leaves would be turning now but here we can't see a single tree and the countryside is so flat." The Westphalian Plain was a featureless landscape, no cover for birds, nor for escaping *Kriegies*. The wind seemed to speed up, racing across the ground like a sprinter in sight of the winning post. Brian shivered, huddling into his greatcoat with his hands in his pockets.

"The view's not much but the company is top notch," said Bob.

In Warburg Brian found school chums, family friends, work associates and contacts of Margery's, a wide circle of acquaintances, although no-one replaced Bob as his closest friend.

"An RAF chap was telling me the other day about a dogfight in the Battle of Britain," said Brian. "It was jolly interesting hearing what we missed. I wonder how much Margery saw of all that."

"I'm glad they were able to stop the Luftwaffe," said Bob. "I was worried back there in Laufen that... you know." Brian nodded, remembering the dreadful *latrinograms* and his fears for Margery and his family; but that was over a year ago and still they hung on back at home.

"I was talking to a fellow from Bomber Command. He was shot down over Germany and had quite an adventure before he was captured," said Brian.

"Mmm, they seem proud of their exploits."

"I think it's different for them, being captured. We weren't prepared for it so waving the white flag seemed shameful, but bomber crews get shot down all the time so it's par for the course for them."

"I suppose so," said Bob. "They've certainly got some tales to tell but they can be a bit snooty, I find, these RAF boys. They're mostly university types from posh public schools and they call us Army chaps 'the brown jobs', you know, on account of our uniforms."

"They love lavatory humour," Brian said. "It can be quite witty. They call those who were captured in Crete 'the ex-Cretians'."

Warburg, December 1941

The days drew in and the frosty weather dried up the mud. One evening the wind screeched around Brian's hut, like wailing voices. Snow by morning I shouldn't wonder, he thought. The boards on the walls were loose, letting the wind in, eddying the dust on the floor and making Brian shiver. He put his hands under his armpits for warmth. Two officers stood by the stove reliving some battle or other.

"I tell you if only they'd sent up the reinforcements when we called for them, it would have been a different story."

"I know, old chap. Bad show. If we'd been able to break through near… "

Brian wished they'd give it a rest; those battles were over and done with but they seemed to be the only topic of conversation for the regular Army officers. They're such a dull crowd, Brian thought; I've had a bellyful of them. He had given up the idea of taking a regular commission after the war.

He tried to study. His father had arranged a correspondence course for his bankers' exams and he needed to pass if he was to continue his career. He wasn't sure though whether he wanted to go back to banking after the war; all he knew was that he wanted to be with Margery. He found it hard to concentrate on his books, sharing the table with blokes writing letters, playing backgammon and mending socks

A jazz record played on the gramophone and Brian's feet tapped as he remembered dancing with Margery. It was no good, he couldn't study tonight so he turned to

Margery's letters. He felt closer to her as he constructed a diary of her wartime life, her day-to-day activities such as taking his sister Doris and little John for a drive with Joey, swimming with Johnnie, Andrew and Norah, and scouring the shops for shoes big enough to fit her feet. He was lost in thought as Charles burst in, bringing the first flurry of snow.

"Have you heard the news?" he said. "The Japanese have attacked Pearl Harbour and the Yanks have come into the war." Study, cards, letters were forgotten, all attention on Charles.

"When did this happen?"

"Have they declared war on Germany too?"

"Were there many casualties?" Charles held up his hand and conveyed the facts to the excited men. Then he left and moved to the next room, the bearer of good tidings. The *Kriegies* buzzed as the implications rippled round the room. At first there was euphoria.

"The Yanks will sort Hitler out."

"He can't beat *them.*"

"Think of the troops they'll be able to mobilise." But then realism crept in, as snow drifted through the thin walls.

"I think this should turn things around... sooner or later."

"Later probably. It will take time." The *Kriegies* batted ideas about like shuttlecocks, as gritty snow scudded against the windows.

"I think the war will last longer... with the Yanks in."

"Damn it, I hoped I'd be home for Christmas." It was always Christmas. Ice began to form on the windows.

"But we are bound to win with the Yanks, aren't we?"

"It's better to take time and win outright than to settle

for peace with Hitler. We can't trust him."

"We mustn't leave unfinished business like they did last time. Best to get the job done properly this time."

Brian listened as the debate went backwards and forwards. Much as he missed Margery, he didn't want the Goons to emerge victorious, nor did he want a cobbled together peace that would settle nothing. He felt he could hang on a bit longer if it meant they'd get a lasting peace for their children, his children and Margery's. That would be worth waiting for.

Warburg, January 1942

The freezing weather gave Brian chilblains on his toes, his fingers and the tops of his ears. He took to wearing a balaclava when he went outside, and his gloves stayed on indoors and outdoors. Frosty weather's good healthy weather, he thought, it kills the germs; Margery was worried about him but Brian stayed fit. The *Kriegies* kept their own company and were rarely ill.

In the middle of the month the post arrived, the first post for nearly two months. It had been disrupted as the Americans, who had organised the Red Cross deliveries, were no longer neutral, and the Swiss had taken over. The arrival of post disturbed the *Kriegies'* equilibrium. Some got letters, some didn't; some heard good news, some bad. Letters reminded the *Kriegies* of home and showed them what they were missing; they brought their loved ones closer while also emphasising the distance between them.

Brian got a batch of four letters from Margery and sorted them by date. He opened the first envelope, drew out the letter and settled down to read. He tensed with fright. Oh no! Johnnie was ill, very ill. Brian's head spun and alarm seeped through him like water through a sponge. With shaking fingers he ripped open the other envelopes; thank goodness several had come together. His eyes scanned the pages for news: Johnnie had pneumonia, was at crisis point, Nellie was with him. By the third letter Johnnie had turned the corner and was out of danger, but the fourth told of a shadow on his lung; he had tuberculosis.

Brian felt powerless. He wanted to be with Margery, to comfort her, to help Johnnie. Damn these Goons for keeping him here! What a tragedy for Johnnie; he had been so witty, so full of fun, always joking and teasing and now… his lungs might be damaged, his life restricted forever. Brian felt useless and Margery needed him.

Tuberculosis was incurable, Brian knew that, but perhaps early treatment might make a difference? Would Nellie be able to afford it? Doctors' fees could be so expensive and she was a widow. Money mustn't stop them, he thought, my money must be their money. I'll tell my father to access my savings, if necessary. It was precious little but it was all he could do, stuck here in Germany. He ached to be with his fiancée and his friend. Captivity had never felt more bitter.

Warburg, April 1942

After the snow came the thaw and the mud set in again. The *Kriegies* dug ditches to drain the parade ground, creating a rugby field and a football pitch where some epic battles were fought. England played Scotland, the RAF against the Army, the Bucks Battalion against the Royal Engineers and so on.

"I was glad to see you win yesterday, Brian," said Bob. "I had a little flutter on your team."

"Well, we did you proud then, old boy. I'd been training hard for that one."

"It was pretty damned close, wasn't it?"

"If they'd scored just one more try that would have been it. We'd never have come back after that."

"I suppose the ground's getting a bit hard for a replay?" said Bob.

"It's nearly the end of the season. But we're digging the pitch to make it soft enough for the finals of the room tournament this weekend."

"Not quite Twickenham, then?" said Bob, chuckling. "By the way, did you see those storks yesterday?"

"I did. They were quite a sight. I'd never seen storks outside a zoo before. The birdwatching brigade were delighted."

One morning Brian noticed a cluster of British troops by the gateway. There was nothing unusual in this as Warburg was used as a staging post for prisoner transport. But something about one of the men caught Brian's attention; he looked familiar so Brian wandered over and found Private Jackson, on route for a new camp.

"How are you doing, Jackson?"

"Not so bad, Sir. There's not much grub but it's got a whole lot better since we got them parcels."

"Do you have any news of the others? What happened to Mills?"

"'e got moved to the 'ospital, Sir. 'is wound opened up like, so the Jerries carted 'im off. I 'aven't seen 'im since.

But I've been with Bert, Sir, Bert Taylor, you remember?" Brian nodded. "Me and Bert was working for this farmer, see, digging potatoes and that. And Jack was with us for a bit, Jack Baker." They chatted away for about ten minutes and Jackson told him about their journey into Germany, their work in the camps and as much as he knew about the other men. It cheered Brian no end to see him again and to hear how his men were faring. Then the Goons came out and Jackson was marched away with the others. Brian stood as near to the gate as he dared, watching his retreating back until he was out of sight.

"You're a lucky man, Brian," said Bob. "I wish I had news about the lads from my company."

Warburg, Summer 1942

The weather got warmer and Brian spent more time out of doors. His mess group had a vegetable plot. The only vegetable the Germans seemed to recognise was the potato and the *Kriegies* joked about getting fat with *kartoffeln* belly. Brian liked hoeing, gently drawing the tool through the soft earth rooting out the weeds and leaving the vegetable seedlings with space to grow. His friend Bill sauntered over to chat.

"Just keep hoeing, old boy, and I can give you a bit more soil," said Bill. Brian noticed that yellow clay was falling slowly from the bottom of Bill's trouser legs. He kept the hoe moving before it was noticed by the Goons. Brian kept his eyes on the ground.

"I suppose it's the spoil from that tunnel you're digging from the bathhouse?"

"That's right. Getting rid of the stuff is a damned nuisance. Your veggie plot is jolly handy."

"We can't put too much in one place. Walk about a bit and pretend you're looking at my seedlings; I'll follow along covering what you spread."

Summer was the escape season, the time of dry days for digging and warm nights for sleeping rough. This year the escapers were particularly active, the Army provided the know-how and the RAF the panache. Brian remembered that Bill had always been bold, courting danger for its adrenalin rush; he was the type to try a tunnel. The *Kriegies* took boards from the beds and the huts until some of them swayed like reeds in the wind. Rademacher, the Chief Security Officer, was always suspicious and had a nasty habit of sending his Goons into a hut in the middle of the night.

"*'Raus, 'raus*," they would shout, pulling blankets off the sleeping men and throwing them out into the night while they ransacked the hut. They were searching for contraband, trowels, spoons, scoops, anything that might be used to dig. Rademacher could make these searches last for hours while the unlucky officers shivered outside in the darkness, powerless to stop the Goons from random acts of spite. One night Brian was furious when he came back into his hut to find that his display of Margery's photos had been ripped off the wall by his bed and left, like confetti, on the floor. Damn Rademacher, he thought, that's just petty spite.

Sometimes the Goons found *verboten* items, and then reprisals followed. Loss of privileges was the usual punishment: no theatre, no library or, worst of all for Brian, no letters. The Goons knew the officers must try to escape –

they would do the same if they were prisoners-of-war – but they were going to make the consequences as unpleasant as possible.

"How far have you got, Bill?" Brian bent to pull up a dandelion.

"We've done about 70 feet and there's another 40 to go. We've been at it about three weeks now."

The whole camp took part in escape activity, directly or indirectly. Brian's speciality was whittling buttons for German uniforms. One day a party of orderlies had marched up to the gates, accompanied by their 'German' guards, *Kriegies* in disguise. They showed their papers to the sentry and went through; Brian's buttons had passed the test.

"What are your chances of making it through the wire?"

"About 50:50, I'd say. The longer we're at it, the greater the chance of it being discovered but I might be lucky, you never know."

Brian knew the success rate was not very high; only five tunnels had made it to the wire so far. Bill's tunnel was discovered at the next search and he and his friends were marched away for two weeks in the cooler, solitary confinement on bread and water. Then the Goons arrived with their usual tunnel filler, liquid sewage. Bile rose in Brian's mouth as the whole camp reeked for days and he kept his handkerchief over his mouth whenever he went outside.

The *Kriegies* dreamed of a copper-bottomed escape plan, one that was swift and Goon-proof, so that they would never notice what was happening… until it was too late. The escapers mused, pondered, fantasised and eventually Jock, already a serial escaper, had a brainwave.

"We're building bookshelves for the library," he said. He and his mates constructed slatted wooden structures, four of them, twelve feet long. The Goons were satisfied with his explanation. The *Kriegies* would never get the 'bookshelves' down a tunnel so where was the harm?

"Can I have a couple of your bed boards, Brian?"

He knew Jock from Laufen; he'd been there – until he tunnelled his way out. He was one of those *Kriegies* who hated restraint; he had to be plotting, planning for freedom.

"Of course, but leave enough to keep my mattress up. I don't want to fall onto Tom in the night." The carpentry continued, bashing, battering, banging. Four huge 'bookshelves' were assembled and everyone knew what was happening – except the Goons. Brian smiled whenever he thought of it. This would show Rademacher.

"When's the Big Night?" Brian asked Elliot.

"It's all set for the end of the month," Elliot said. "They're going to have a dummy run with the lights next week. It's all going according to plan."

"How many are they hoping to get out?"

"They've settled on 40. The Escape Committee thought any more was too ambitious; it's been hard enough collecting food, clothes and papers for that lot."

"Well, good luck to them." Brian counted the days, tense, excited, waiting. At 10pm on 30th August, the camp plunged into darkness. Forty officers crept from a hut carrying the four 'bookshelves' towards to the wire.

"This is it," said Brian and he started counting the seconds. "One... two... three... four..." The longer the lights were out, the more men could escape – over the wire.

"18... 19... 20..." The escapers turned their

'bookshelves' into scaling ladders and climbed up towards the top.

"31... 32... 33..." The camp orchestra practised, their clamour blanketing the noise. A few escapers went down the other side and disappeared.

"55... 56... 57..." The camp remained in darkness as more officers vanished.

"72... 73... 74..." The *Kriegies* shouted fake orders in German and the Goons ran this way and that, their attention on the electrics not the wire. Up, over, down the other side of the wire went 28 officers and others followed.

"85... 86... 87..." One 'bookshelf' collapsed, stranding a few escapers on the wire.

"88... 89... 90..." counted Brian as the lights came back on, illuminating the remaining officers blinking in the glare.

"Crikey!" said Brian, the next morning. "What a turn up for the books! Twenty eight men out all in one go."

"It's the biggest escape so far. The Warburg Wire Job we're calling it," said Bob and the two men wandered over to look at the notice pinned to one of the ladders.

'Another great British evacuation' it read. The camp was jubilant.

"They say Rademacher's being drafted to the Russian front."

"Just in time for winter," said Brian and they smiled at each other.

The next day they were moved, marching out of Warburg for another camp.

CHAPTER 21

England, April 1942

"Let me carry the tea things out to the kitchen, Mum. Norah can come and chat to me while I get ready," said Margery.

"What time is Donald picking you up?"

"About 6.30 but I need to change my frock and put on a bit of make-up before he gets here."

The two girls went out, leaving Nellie and Norah's mother in an uneasy *tête-à-tête.* Margery knew they didn't have much in common. The link had been their fathers, who had been friends when they first came to Slough as young men out to make their fortunes. And they did, each in his own way; Margery's father, Herbert, did well in the building trade while Norah's father married a girl with money. That came with a price ticket, though, as Joe found out when he had to put up with her airs and graces.

"A girl with her nose in the air is not for me," Herbert said but, after he died, Joe had taken Margery under his wing.

"She'll be good for Norah. Ginger her up a bit." The two girls became chums, in and out of each other's houses like butterflies.

"Did Johnnie get back all right?" Norah asked.

"Yes. It was a slow journey but he reached Maidstone in time to report to his senior officer. He's on light duties and he's not pleased about being a paper wallah."

Margery looked in her wardrobe and took out a cotton frock with a floral pattern. She noticed the box with Brian's letters sitting on the shelf, over two years of letters, their link until he returned. Norah sat on the narrow bed and watched.

"Poor old Johnnie. He got quite annoyed last time he took me out. Mother made such a fuss when we were late back. We were only a teeny bit late but she was waiting up, as she always does. She blamed Johnnie, of course, and gave him quite a ticking off."

Margery knew about the upset as Johnnie had blown his top the next morning. He felt aggrieved that Norah's mother didn't trust him, thought him not good enough for her daughter when they'd been going steady since before the war. Margery could see his point.

"Mother thinks I'm too young to be settling down. She thinks I should go out with other men and look around a bit first."

"What do you think, Norah?" Margery stepped into the clean dress and began to do up the buttons.

"I like Johnnie an awful lot. He's terrific fun. But Mother keeps asking all these other men to dinner or to come to the theatre and I have to go along with it." Norah looked down at her hands and fidgeted.

"I think we've both been brought up to think we've got to do what's expected of us. You know, toe the line and let our parents take the decisions. But at the hospital I see young women with different lives. They have careers, they're earning and in control, if you know what I mean."

"Mother's not too keen on me working at the hospital either."

"She doesn't have much choice though. You've got to do war work."

"Yes, but she thinks scrubbing floors is beneath me. I

should be driving officers around and meeting a better class of person, she says."

"What do you think, Norah?" Norah bit her lip and frowned while Margery looked in the mirror and started to brush her hair.

"I suppose if I had a choice I wouldn't do it but... there's a war on." Norah spread her hands and looked at her friend. Margery enjoyed working at the hospital, loved the feeling that she could help the patients and relished the friendships she'd made; having a life of her own made her feel independent. Norah was going to lose Johnnie if she kept on being such a doormat but Margery felt powerless. Best to change the subject.

"Does this lipstick go with my dress?" she asked. "I don't want it to clash."

"It's just the right shade; it picks up the colour of those flowers. What are you and Donald going to do?"

"We're going to the flicks. Bette Davis is playing in *Little Foxes* at the Odeon."

"Even though Brian's away you always seem to have a partner, Peter or Donald or Andrew. You're so lucky."

"Yes, it's fun. You know what Norah? It's strange the way it's all turned out. I worried about marrying Brian on his first leave back in 1940; I wanted to do a bit more gadding about, enjoy my girlhood – it only comes once in a lifetime after all. It was horrid, of course, when he got captured and I was wretched. But now it's all settled down and we can write so I can have my fun."

"Does Brian mind?"

"No, he doesn't want me to sit here doing nothing for the whole war. It's dreary enough without that. Now which belt shall I wear?" She held up two belts, one red, one blue, against her waist and looked in the mirror.

"I think the blue one is best."

"Smashing. I'm ready then."

England, June 1942

The phone woke Margery up. She leapt out of bed and padded down the hall. Whoever could it be at this time in the morning? Five thirty, the hall clock said.

"Brookwood 2323."

"Curly, thank God it's you."

"Johnnie. What's the matter? Are you all right?"

"Yes, *I* am. But I've got bad news, the worst sort of news. It's Andrew, you see."

"Andrew? What's happened? Has he been hurt?"

"There was an accident, a dreadful accident." He paused and Margery filled with dread. "You know he was training for these special commando raids? Well, he was on an exercise last night with live ammunition." He hesitated and Margery began to shiver. "You see Curly, he was killed – by mistake."

Margery was silent; she wondered if she'd heard right. Andrew had been part of their family, had partnered her at dances, at supper parties, had been a good friend and now… Johnnie said he was gone.

"Are you sure, Johnnie?" It was a meaningless thing to say but she was stunned, like a wasp that went on sucking jam even after you had cut it in half.

"Yes, old girl. I *am* sure, unfortunately."

Margery struggled with disbelief, too numb to speak.

"Look, Curly, I'll be home later today to pick up some things. I've got to go to Scotland to see his people. It's a wretched business and it'll be a dreadful shock for them. He was their only child, you know."

"Oh Johnnie, that's a hard number. Poor you! Is there anything I can do?"

"Yes, you can tell Mum. Break it to her gently, Curly. She was very fond of Andrew. We all were. I've got to go now." The pips sounded.

"Right-ho Johnnie. Bye." Margery replaced the receiver and the line went dead. Her mind was empty, her heart thumping, her ears ringing as if she had heard a loud bang. Perhaps if she didn't move it wouldn't be true. But that was a child's game, and she wasn't a child any longer. This was real. She must think what to do. Nellie had not stirred; her hearing was not what it used to be and she must have missed the phone.

Margery realised she was trembling, with shock and with cold. There was a wicked draught in the hall and she was only in her nightie. She'd better fetch her slippers and her dressing gown and then she'd put the kettle on. Perhaps a drop of brandy wouldn't come amiss; she knew Nellie kept some in the cupboard for medicinal purposes. She could make a cup of tea and take a cup to Nellie in a bit.

Then suddenly, she came out of her stupor and the news winded her, knocked the stuffing out of her. She felt angry. This wretched war! It was taking everyone she cared about. Johnnie said it was an accident; that meant it should never have happened. It wasn't fair that she had to grow up in these terrible times. Why couldn't she have an ordinary girlhood?

Then the tears came, hot bitter tears for Andrew, for Brian, for her youth. This was another loss, another absence. Would she have any friends left by the time the war ended? She cried and cried and then she started to make the tea. The mundane task eased her. There was nothing to be done; it was as it was.

Margery lay in bed listening to the rain drumming on the window. The blackout blinds were drawn, the room dark and it was hard to tell whether it was day or night.

"It's doctor's orders," Nellie said. "To save your eyes."

Margery remembered being sent home from the hospital.

"You're far too ill to work, Nurse Street," Sister had said. "Go home and call the doctor or I'll have to find you a bed on the isolation ward."

She had caught measles, another of those wretched childhood diseases. She felt miserable, itchy and tearful, like a fractious baby. The doctor had said she was thoroughly run down and she was to stay in bed until her temperature went down. That was fine as all she wanted to do was sleep. But she couldn't rest properly; her dreams were nightmares. Andrew's face kept appearing, smiling at her, hiding from her, chasing her. He was spinning round in her head and he seemed to be trapped there.

The funeral had been dreadful, Johnnie said. Andrew's mother wept and his father tried to keep a stiff upper lip but somehow that seemed worse. Margery had written to his parents, to tell them how sorry she was, but, however hard she tried, the phrases rang hollow. Words could only skim the surface on the deep pool of her emotion.

'He was a very fine young man,' she said. He was in so many ways, but that was poor comfort for his parents when he was gone.

'I will never forget how kind he was when Johnnie was ill and we needed a friend.' She remembered he had said that Johnnie's illness might be a blessing in disguise. How ironic that Johnnie had pulled through, but Andrew had fallen.

'I will always think of him with admiration.' It was true, but admiration was a poor substitute for the real thing, that lively, fun-loving, upright person that had been Andrew. He would never again duck her in the swimming pool, never teach her to march, never laugh with her at Johnnie's jokes. These thoughts were whirling around in her fevered brain as she tossed and turned on her hot sheets in the darkened room.

Johnnie was having a bad time too. He was still weak from TB and he had been through hell with Andrew's funeral; they had been close and his death had been sudden. After that, he seemed to have lost his way, as if he was steering a different course but it had gone wrong. He had come into her room yesterday morning to talk while he drank his tea.

It was hard for her frenzied mind to make sense of his babblings. He talked of living each day to the full, about focusing on the present, of enjoying himself while he still could and it seemed to be mixed up with Norah. It was odd as the two of them had been so attached for a long time. Norah's mother had been petty, he said.

"You know Norah's not allowed to stay out late, not after midnight. I find you an unreliable young man," she had said. Johnnie would usually rise above her snide remarks, but it was different when he was grieving. He had answered back.

"I think there are bigger things in life than that. It doesn't really matter whether she comes in at 12 or 12.30, does it?" Mrs Walker hadn't liked that and said he must mend his manners if he wanted to pay court to Norah.

"I'm damned if I will, Curly," he said. "I can't take any more of it, I can tell you. Norah ought to stand up for herself."

Margery was too weak to argue, to plead Norah's case and now he was taking Paddy Jones to the dance at the Pantiles. Not Norah – Paddy! Oh what a muddle! If only her head would stop spinning, she might be able to think straight.

England, October 1942

Margery waited for her eyes to adjust. The faux Tudor leaded window only let in a little light and the restaurant was saving electricity for the evening. She was wearing a pale blue twinset and the string of pearls that Nellie had given her for her twenty-first birthday. A little blue hat on the back of her head completed the outfit. She had been to have some photos taken to send to Brian for his Christmas present. She saw Brenda, Brian's closest sister, hanging up her coat, and she gave a little wave.

"It was such a good idea to meet for lunch, Margery," said Brenda. "It gives us a chance to catch up."

Margery hadn't seen much of Brenda; she had been working in Oxford since the war began but now she was married and had moved back to Ditham Croft.

"A table for two, please," said Margery. As the waitress started to lead them towards the back of the room, Margery noticed her legs; she had dyed them brown and drawn a line up the back to look like the seam on stockings. Real silk stockings were precious, far too expensive to wear to work.

"Could we have that table at the window, please?" Margery said.

"Oh, that one's reserved. We always save it for Mrs Forbes-Newton."

"But she's not here and it's one o'clock." Margery noticed Brenda making a face, a very Dowling face. Her expression mirrored Brian's when he didn't want a fuss.

"I'll ask the manager," said the waitress. There was a hurried whispering by the desk, then the waitress tossed her head and led them to the table in the window. They sat and perused the menu; it looked as appetising as chicken food, Margery thought.

"I'll have the soup," said Brenda. "What about you?"

"The vegetable hotpot," said Margery. They placed their order and settled down to gossip.

"Tell me all about your wedding, Brenda. What did you wear? Where did you go for your honeymoon?"

"It was a very quiet affair and I was so sorry you couldn't come."

"I just couldn't get the time off, I'm afraid."

"We didn't give you much notice. It was such a hurry because Gordon was being posted overseas and we wanted to get married before he went."

"Of course, I understand. I hear that you've given up your job. Do you miss it?"

"Well, I do. But actually I think I'm going to have my hands full soon." Brenda looked down at her stomach and Margery's eyes followed her glance, noticing the bump.

"Oh, Brenda. How terrific. I didn't know." For Margery, the news was bittersweet. Brenda hadn't been engaged when Brian had proposed and now she was a bride and soon to be a mother. Margery pulled herself together. "When's it due?"

"Not until March but it seemed best for me to move back to Mummy and Daddy and wait there while Gordon's away. It's company for me and it's good for Mummy. She's been feeling a bit lost since the war started."

"I'm so pleased for you."

"We hope you'll be godmother, Margery." Brenda's smile was sun on golden corn. She's so pretty thought Margery. She's a little elf while I feel like a heffalump. *Piglet and the Heffalump*, she had always enjoyed that story. What fun it would be to read those stories to a child, her child, Brian's child. She felt chuffed to bits for Brenda but… she wished she could get on with her life, like other girls.

"Buck up, Margery. The war will soon be over now the Americans have come in. Brian will come home and then you'll have a baby; they'll be cousins." Margery hoped that would come true, that it would turn out well in the end but sometimes she had such dark thoughts about Brian. Worry was never far from the surface.

"Tell me your news," Brenda said. "Daddy says that Brian's in this camp where they've had this big break-out. Is that true?"

"Yes, he was there but he's been moved now. They all

have. I've just got his new address. He couldn't say anything about the escape of course."

"No, I can see that."

"Tell me, what's all this about Johnnie? I hear he's got a new girlfriend, Paddy Jones."

"Yes, it has been a bit of a surprise. We more or less grew up with Paddy. The Jones's used to take the house next door to us at Sandbanks when we were children so Johnnie and Paddy knew each other well back in those days and then they met up again while he was ill and that was that. Cupid's arrows and all that stuff."

Margery made light of it but Norah was her closest friend and she couldn't help feeling Johnnie had betrayed her. She knew Norah was heartbroken because he had been going out with her for such a long time. Paddy was so sexy with her simpering ways and flirtatious glances. She seemed to have bewitched Johnnie as surely as Anne Boleyn had bewitched King Henry VIII. Margery was vexed but she didn't show her feelings to Brenda; she didn't want to appear uncharitable. The only person with whom she shared her views was Brian; she knew he'd understand.

CHAPTER 22

Eichstätt, September 1942

Brian's spirits rose as they marched into the tree-lined valley; this looks like a change for the better, he thought. Throughout their journey the *Kriegie* rumour mill had been working overtime and Brian listened as he sat on the hard wooden bench.

"They're going to keep us on a tight rein because of the Wire Job..."

"I've heard they've got these *Strafe Lager*, punishment camps..."

"We're going to a luxury camp with a swimming pool..."

Brian didn't know what to think. He looked out of the window and watched the scenery as the Westphalian Plain gave way to broken country with hills, fields and woods.

"Wait and see, wait and see," the train wheels seemed to sing as they trundled along the track. In the late afternoon the train stopped at a small halt beside a ridge covered with pine trees.

"*'Raus, 'raus*," the guards called and Brian and Bob gathered their kitbags, stepped onto the platform and lined up. As they marched along, the September sunshine slanted through the trees, freckling the road with shadows and when they approached the camp's gates the evening sun tinted the brick buildings with rosy light.

"I think we've hit it lucky this time," said Bob.

"I'm glad to be amongst trees again." Brian had found the flat Westphalian Plain constraining, limiting his horizons and his dreams. Their new camp lay beside the Altmühl and Brian saw cherry trees, lime trees and birch trees as they marched along the valley. Across the river the bank rose steeply to a limestone bluff, covered with firs and spruces.

Morale was high, floating on the bubble of the Warburg Wire Job and the thrill of the journey. We're like schoolboys on a day out or a flock of little birds in the sunshine, Brian thought as a charm of goldfinches flitted out of a cherry tree.

They lined up on the parade ground for the introductory address by the Camp Commandant, Herr Oberst-Lieutenant Blätterbauer. Blätters, as the *Kriegies* called him, was a small, rotund officer with legs too short for his body; he waddled up and down like Donald Duck quacking out his list of *verboten* instructions. Brian had picked up enough German to get the gist of the camp rules; *verboten* to be late for *Appell*, *verboten* to feed the guard dogs, *verboten* to try and escape, *verboten* to attend *Appell* without jackets, and so on. The officers jeered and heckled as Blätters told them that he would run his camp with military precision; insolence and sloppiness would not be tolerated.

Brian was allocated to Block 1, right beside the commander's office, the *Kommandatur*. As he was marched across the parade ground to his new quarters, a blackbird trilled from a lime tree and Brian's heart sang too as he saw that their rooms had electricity, washing facilities and a vegetable garden. Although he was sorry to have left his RAF friends behind, this camp promised to be better than Warburg and he looked forward to fresh faces.

He noted the untidy clutter, the smell of cigarette smoke, wet washing and burnt food as he entered the room.

A jazz record played on the gramophone... loudly. The room had about ten bunks, two tiers high, and he saw officers reading, chatting and writing letters. He knew the ropes now: find a bunk, unpack his belongings, introduce himself to his roommates.

"Is this bunk free?" Brian asked an officer lounging idly on a top bunk.

"It sure is," he said. Brian noticed his accent as he put his kitbag down beside the bed. It had an American inflection but without the twang he associated with the Yanks.

"Hey there, I'm Bud."

"I'm Brian, Brian Dowling. Pleased to meet you." Brian held out his hand. Bud hesitated slightly and then shook it, a good firm handshake. "Where are you from?"

"Well I guess you'd say Canada." Bud ran his hand over his crew cut. "We've only been here a few days. We launched a raid in France, some place called Di-ep-pe." He rolled each syllable over his tongue, as if the taste and texture were unfamiliar. "We were told it would be a piece of cake but..." He shrugged his shoulders and raised his eyebrows. "We were meant to give the Hun a real surprise, show them we could land in France, have a recce and then get out but... it was like they were waiting for us. I guess some guy tipped them off."

"Probably the French," said Brian. "It sounds to have been a bad show." If the Allies couldn't launch a successful raid on the French coast, it was going to be some time until they could open a Western Front. Brian thought he'd better settle in here; he would be waiting some time.

"How many of you Canadians are here?"

"Gee, there's a whole bunch of us. Chuck and Billy are

over there. What happened to you, Brian?"

"Oh, that was the French too. I was captured near Dunkirk when they let the Germans through. That was back in May 1940, two years, three months and five days ago to be precise." Brian kept a careful tally of his time as a *Kriegie;* it was like making up the ledger at the bank. He sighed and shook his head, bemused by how long his captivity had lasted.

"Gee whiz, that sure is some long stretch. I guess I can learn a few tricks about camp life from you."

When Brian had unpacked, he sat at the table with Bud, smoking. Bud told him about Canada, the lakes, the wide open prairies and the Rocky Mountains. Brian was intrigued and added Canada to the list of places he wanted to visit with Margery after the war. Bud also had recent news from England; he had spent a year in Kent, training as a commando, and he was married to a girl from Guildford.

"Your folks in England must be having a real hard time." Bud shook his head. "I couldn't get my head round it when I first came over, the blackout, the rationing, those air-raid shelters and only a couple of inches of bathwater."

It was so long since Brian had been home that he hadn't appreciated the extent of the changes. Although he knew Margery helped in the hospital, he hadn't appreciated that women drove lorries, worked in shipyards and served in the Army. Bud's stories made him feel he had missed so much. The bombing had reduced areas of London to rubble, Bud said. These were the details that Margery couldn't put in her letters. It sounded like a different country, more humdrum, more regimented, more uniform. Would the England he remembered ever come back or had the war damaged it beyond repair? Time was passing and life was changing while he was stuck here, waiting, waiting for the Allies to win the war.

No sooner had Brian made friends with Bud than they were separated. The Goons buzzed into Block 1 like a swarm of bees.

"*'Raus, 'raus,*" they shouted. Brian was beginning to wonder if that was all they could say. They were jumpy, swinging their guns around as they ordered the British *Kriegies* to pack up and march out. Bother, thought Brian, I was just settling in and now I've got to start all over again. I wonder what's up. The next morning at *Appell*, the Canadian *Kriegies* arrived with their hands shackled in front of their bodies and the whole camp was outraged.

"It's retaliation," Elliot said, as he walked round the parade ground with Brian. The leaves on the lime trees were changing colour, turning yellow, then brown as the nights got colder. "The Goons have some story that the Canadians handcuffed their prisoners so they're getting their own back."

"It's brutal. Surely it must be against the Geneva Convention? What's the SBO doing?"

"He's furious, of course, and he's issued a formal protest to Blätters but he won't demean himself to negotiate about such a barbaric custom. Apparently though, the orders have come from Hitler himself."

"He's nothing but a thug, but if that's the case, I suppose that there's not much the old boy can do about it." Brian offered Elliot a cigarette.

"No, but he's referred the matter to the War Office and it's being taken up at diplomatic level. It's reached the press back home and they're making quite a fuss." They're throwing conkers into the bonfire and watching them pop, thought Brian. Margery will be worried though; I must tell her it isn't me.

"In one way I feel pleased," said Elliot. "It's good to hear the government hasn't completely forgotten about us *Kriegies.*"

Brian nodded. They had felt abandoned; the Dunkirk story had been about the men who got home, about the brave little ships saving the British Army and everyone at home ignored the plight of those, like Brian and Elliot, who had held the corridor and been taken prisoner. Now they had been reminded of their existence and it was good to be back in the limelight.

"Yes, that's true." Brian blew out a cloud of smoke. He left Elliot and walked towards Block 1 to pay Bud a visit, but the Goon on the door held up his rifle and shouted:

"*Nein, nein. Kein Eintritt.*" That's pretty clear; no entrance. The Canadians were to be isolated, not allowed to mix, and forced to cope alone with life in handcuffs. It must be hard, thought Brian, and so humiliating.

Eichstätt, October 1942

A few weeks later the guards came to Brian's room with their regular refrain:

"*'Raus, 'raus.*" This time Brian was ordered to move back into Block 1 with the Canadians. The Goons lined Brian up with the other *Kriegies* and shouted: "*Hände, Hände.*" Clattering and clanking, they passed along the line locking each man into their chains. It's like harnessing the horses, Brian thought, his mind going back to Margery hitching Joey to the harrow. He tried to scratch his head and found he had to use both hands. It was the same with eating his meals, writing a letter, lighting a cigarette, whatever he did with his right hand, the left had to do too. It'll take a bit of time to get the hang of these ordinary little jobs, he thought. He looked at his hands linked by a short chain and thought of games of cops and robbers when it was always the Baddies who were led away in handcuffs. But now it was him in shackles and it felt demeaning. Besides, it was awkward; he cut himself, opening a tin of sardines.

"Damn and blast it!" He threw down the tin, lifted both arms and stuck his finger in his mouth. "These Goons are traitors; they sign the Geneva Convention then disregard it when it suits them. They're savages."

"Put a brave face on it," said Bill. "If we get angry that gives them an excuse for further atrocities." Brian nodded, seeing the point. It was ironic that he'd gone to fight for freedom and found himself in shackles; the very word evoked images of dungeons and torture and he knew that Margery would be shocked when she found out. I must make light of it when I write, he thought; I don't want her to worry about me. I'll say it's an inconvenience but, after all, it's not painful nor life threatening.

"I've just about sorted out how to climb onto my bunk, write letters and cook my meals," said Bill. "But wiping my bum defeats me."

"Me too, old boy," said Brian. "I asked the chap on the next seat to do it for me and I reciprocated."

"Anyway, Brian, we can still have a game of bridge," said Bill. "Are you on for this afternoon?"

"That sounds just the ticket."

Despite the chains, morale rose when Jimmy, the illicit camp radio, brought news of Montgomery's victory at El Alamein. *'This is not the end. It is not even the beginning of the end but it is, perhaps, the end of the beginning.'* Churchill's words heartened Brian.

"Good old Monty," said Bill. "Now we've got them on the run in Africa, it'll be Italy next, you'll see."

Brian was glad of the shift towards the Allies. Until now the news had reported German victories; now it was the Allies' turn. Next they heard about the Eastern Front; how the Russian Army had withdrawn, luring the Huns deeper and deeper into their country. They had outflanked the German Army and besieged them in Stalingrad in the depths of a Russian winter.

"Rademacher must be having a pretty tough time of it," said Bill.

"Serve him right." Brian remembered what his thugs had done to Margery's photos. "This sounds like the turning point."

"Perhaps we'll be home by Christmas." Bill winked at Brian; they had both heard that line so many times. Still, the news of Stalingrad was promising. If the Allies are making progress, maybe I should begin to plan for life after the war. Until now, the end had seemed remote; he'd dreamed of picnics, parties and primroses, misty insubstantial images, floating like shadows on the wind. He dreamed of living with Margery in a little cottage in the country, spending his evenings sitting by the fire while she knitted. He hugged this picture close; it was something to wish for, something to look forward to. These pleasures won't spoil, he thought.

If the war was moving towards its conclusion, he needed to be realistic. Pipedreams were fine in the camps but, when the time came and he went home, he'd need a job, a good job to support them both. Perhaps he should try those bankers' exams again. Even if he didn't go back to the bank, he'd be in a better position with a professional qualification; book-keeping, accountancy, and commercial law would never come amiss. He was a slow learner – he spent too long pondering the possibilities – but in the camp he had time, all the time in the world. It's best to get those exams out of the way, he thought, and it's something I can do in chains.

Since the war had begun to turn, Blätters encouraged education, anything to keep the *Kriegies* busy and keep their minds off tunnels. The *Kriegies* could follow correspondence courses and sit their exams under supervision. The SBO set up an Education Committee and they organised a system; *Kriegies* with qualifications tutored those without. Brian knew that other men studied; John continued his Philosophy degree, Bill studied Law, while David learned Russian. Elliot was on the Education Committee and he came to see Brian.

"I've found Nick," he said. "He used to work in a Foreign Exchange department and he's in Block 1 too. He's willing to tutor you for that exam, Brian." It made all the difference; Nick used practical examples to explain the theory and Brian got the hang of it and worked towards his future with Margery so that, when the end of the war came, he would be ready to look after her.

Eichstätt, Christmas 1942

The greatest trial for Brian was not the shackles but the segregation. Even when they went to watch a football match, the Block 1 *Kriegies* had to stand apart from the others. Brian missed his old messmates, his companions from the battalion and Bob, his best friend from the beginning of his captivity. It got him down, being restricted to his room, to the same company day after day. Bud paced up and down, Tom complained endlessly, Bill liked tin-bashing while Chuck played hymns on the gramophone and, through all of this, Brian studied. The *Kriegies* were pebbles on a beach, rubbing up against each other with the swash and backwash of the waves and, although Brian tried to keep himself to himself, that was hard when he was living at such close quarters.

Christmas Day was a real treat; the Goons left them without shackles from Christmas Eve until Boxing Day morning, free to socialise with the rest of the camp.

"It makes it a real holiday," said Bill.

"It's funny how ordinary things become special if you're denied them." Brian called on Bob, taking a few cigarettes with him and they sat side by side on Bob's bunk.

"Well, Bob, here we are again, our third Christmas. How's Norah?"

"She's doing well, thank you. How are you getting on over there in Block 1?"

"It's OK, when you get the hang of it." Brian rubbed his wrists.

"Are you going to the panto?"

"Yes, it sounds fun. *Babes Up*, I believe it's called. We're allowed to go but we aren't supposed to mix." Brian winked at Bob to show how likely it was that the rule would be obeyed. "Now tell me all the camp news."

"Well, Jock is back with us." Bob raised his eyebrows. "The Goons picked him up after the Wire Job, but he's undaunted, cracking on with *another* tunnel."

"Not quite the weather for it, I'd say."

"No, you're right. I think they're going to give it a break until the spring."

"These restless types have to have something on the go, don't they?" Brian thought that the serial escapers like Jock and Rupert got their kicks from the whole process, planning, digging, disposing of the spoil, preparing their getaway; escaping kept them going, like whisky for a drunkard or betting for a gambler.

"I don't know why they bother," said Bob. "I'd rather sit it out and wait for the end of the war."

"Escaping's not my bag either. I'm planning my future with Margery and getting down to my studying at last."

When Brian sat his exams, he sailed through the foreign exchange paper, thanks to Nick. But two subjects remained outstanding: Accountancy and English. As Education Officer, Elliot visited to review his progress.

"I can manage the English," Brian said. "But I really need some help with Accountancy."

"I know you do, old boy." Elliot rubbed his chin. "But it's a bit of a poser. You see there's no-one in chains with a relevant qualification and the Goons won't let you mix with the others."

CHAPTER 23

England, December 1942

Margery sat in the church with Nellie waiting for the bride. She was late; she'd make more of a stir that way. They waited in their pew looking at the stained glass windows behind the altar while Johnnie fidgeted at the front where he stood with his Best Man; that would have been Brian if he'd been here. Margery had seen his parents, sitting three rows back in their best clothes. Margery looked at her watch; she was ten minutes overdue. What could be keeping her?

Theirs had been a whirlwind romance. Johnnie had never looked back after that dance at the Pantiles. He was obsessed with Paddy, all thoughts of Norah gone and Nellie had encouraged him; she and Daisy Jones were a double act, conniving to bring the young people together. Nellie treated Paddy as a daughter, a favoured daughter, Margery thought.

Margery felt uneasy. Norah had been her friend, was still her friend – but Paddy was… something else. She had known Paddy since childhood. They had played, bickered, dreamed, and drifted. Their relationship had been close but never straightforward; they were not friends but were bound together by family, fondness and feelings, strong feelings.

Paddy had always been naughty, full of mischief. She was the youngest in her family and had got away with behaviour for which Margery would have been punished. She remembered the incident of the velvet dresses, those frocks that little girls wore at parties. Margery's and Paddy's dresses were not soft, silky and smooth; they were coarse, hot and scratchy. They hated them. One night,

Paddy had looked at her dress draped by the door and said: "I'm not going to wear it! They can't make me."

"Oh yes they can!" Margery was older and wiser.

"Not if I cut it up, they can't."

Margery didn't believe she really would but Paddy tiptoed downstairs, came back with the kitchen scissors and cut into the skirt. This was too much so, belatedly, Margery went to find the adults. Paddy was scolded, but so was Margery – for not stopping her. As if she could: Paddy was a law unto herself. To add insult to injury, Paddy could not use her velvet dress and was allowed to wear a comfortable cotton frock while Margery continued to itch in velvet through many a family festivity.

The first notes of the *Bridal March* brought Margery out of her daydream. Here she was – at last. Everyone stood as Paddy swept up the aisle, simpering on her father's arm.

"Dearly Beloved, we are gathered together here in the sight of God and in the face of this congregation to join together this man and this woman in Holy Matrimony..."

When would it be her turn? When would those words ring out for her? It was hard to watch Paddy in her lovely dress, with her bridesmaids and her little page boy. It was three years since Brian had proposed, three years of waiting. She had had her fun, her gadding about, and she was ready to settle down. It seemed invidious; Paddy was younger than her but she was getting married first. She always managed to steal the limelight and leave Margery in the shadows.

England, February 1943

"It makes perfect sense for Paddy to move in with us," Nellie said. "I'll have company while you're at work and she'll be here when Johnnie's home so there's no need for him to go see her."

Nellie wanted to keep her son close; he might be married but he was still her boy. So Paddy moved into Stone Cottage, a queen ascending her throne, using Johnnie's room while he lived at the officers' mess in Aldershot. He was not fit for active service so he was a staff officer passing the time in a mountain of paperwork.

Back in the 1930s, Nellie, Johnnie and Margery had been happy together, joking and teasing, bringing their friends home and enjoying each other's company. Since Johnnie went into the Army, Margery and Nellie had settled into a comfortable mother-daughter relationship with chats about patients, village gossip, and plans for shopping trips. But now there was Paddy, a cuckoo in the nest.

One evening, Margery came off duty, tired, cold and hungry. She made her way down the garden to find Joey, put him in the stable and feed him, before she came into the kitchen for dinner. Usually Nellie would make a cup of tea and listen to her gossip, garnering titbits like an acquisitive magpie. But this evening the kitchen was in disarray. There was no sign of dinner; teacups and plates were piled on the draining board while Paddy and Nellie were sitting at the table, laughing and smoking. Judy wagged her tail as Margery bent down to stroke her silky ears.

"Has Judy been fed, Mum?"

"No, not yet. We've been busy." Margery broke up some dry bread, mixed it with gravy and put it on the floor for Judy who gulped it down. Nellie and Paddy were still laughing at a story Paddy was telling. Paddy never fed Judy, never washed up, never helped with the animals.

"What's for dinner, Mum?"

"Oh goodness me, is it that time already?" Nellie heaved herself to her feet and turned towards the stove. "We've had such a party this afternoon. Daisy Jones came over with Kate and we've had a good old girls' gossip. The time has run away from me. I'd better get on, I suppose." Margery had been working and her stomach felt empty; she really did want her supper.

"Can I help, Mum?" Margery felt that Paddy should help, should offer to do the washing up and should learn to cook, but she never did.

"No, it won't take long. The vegs are already done and I've just got to put on the eggs." Paddy lit another cigarette while Margery laid the table.

"I'm looking forward to Johnnie coming home tomorrow," said Paddy. "I'd like to see this new exhibition in London if he can get leave."

Paddy was sophisticated, artistic and cultured; she spoke French and knew about the Arts. Last week she and Johnnie sat close together on the sofa and discussed paintings all Sunday afternoon.

"What do you think about Monet's paintings?" Johnnie had said.

"He does such wonderful things with light. He's good as long as you like lily ponds."

Johnnie had laughed and tickled her chin. Margery didn't even know who Monet was; unlike Paddy, she hadn't been to finishing school in Switzerland. It felt as if Paddy and Johnnie were in a magic circle, while Margery was left outside.

Nellie served dinner and Paddy toyed with her food, pushing it around her plate.

"I should really be on a diet." She pouted and put her head on one side. "But Johnnie says he likes me like this. You never seem to get fat, Curly." Margery wasn't sure she liked Paddy calling her 'Curly'; it was Johnnie's nickname for her, a special brother-sister thing.

"It's because I'm on my feet all day long. You ought to try it."

"Maybe, I will. I was thinking about doing a bit of war work." Margery's throat clenched. Not at the hospital, please; that was her private world.

"Can I help you with the dishes, Mum?"

"Well, if you wash, I can dry and we'll soon be done."

"I think I'll have a bath, Mum," said Margery, a day or two later. She had just come in from her shift and looked forward to a soak in her two inches of water before going dancing.

"Oh, I don't think there's any water left. Paddy's just had a bath." Margery knew Paddy had no scruples about exploiting her ambiguous position in the household – not guest, not family member.

"We're off to the Pantiles with a party of Johnnie's Army friends." Paddy sat at the kitchen table in her dressing gown, waving her hands around as the nail varnish dried. "It'll be such fun; they all adore me, you know." Margery had seen them gawping at Paddy, laughing as she leaned towards them, vying with each other to light her cigarette. To Margery, it seemed disrespectful; she was Johnnie's wife after all.

"Where are you going, Curly?"

"To the Pantiles, with my hospital friends."

"Oh that'll be fun," said Paddy but Margery wasn't so sure; she wished they were going somewhere else.

At the dance, the two parties dropped into friendly rivalry, like puppies play fighting. They bantered across the room and took chairs from each other's tables; there were never enough seats at the Pantiles. Margery returned to her table, breathless after a lively quickstep, to find that her wine glass had disappeared. Johnnie was sitting nearby and, as she caught his eye, he raised his glass to her.

"Your very good health, Curly! You've got excellent taste in wine."

He was toasting her with her own drink. She was used to pranks from her brother – that was normal – but then Paddy sniggered and that rankled. She wished she could get over her anger, her envy, but she couldn't however hard she tried. The only person who understood was Brian.

'I too cannot fight down a wee bit of envy,' he wrote. '*But our time will come soon and time can take nothing from these joys when we do share them.'* That was comforting; his words were a magic spell, easing her pain.

Paddy was bored; she needed to mingle, to hear the gossip, to see people so she decided to sign up for war work. That's a good idea thought Margery; it'll keep her out of mischief. But Paddy wanted to work at Woking Hospital – with her.

"It'll be useful to learn about nursing. Johnnie's still far from well, you know." Margery did know but the hospital was her patch. Margery was serious about her job; good nursing was the key to recovery. She worked hard and she had achieved a great deal; even the strictest of ward sisters trusted her now.

The other Nurse Street was quite different. Paddy was dilettante; she was witty, entertaining and flirtatious, enjoying chit-chat, with the soldiers and the young doctors. At home, Margery listened as Paddy complained about the smell of the bedpans, the tiresome requests from patients, the orders from Sister. She had to laugh at Paddy's stories about flaunting the regulations but…

"Rules are there for a reason, Paddy," said Margery.

"Oh Curly! You're always so solemn. 'Yes Sister' 'No, Sister'. Me, I just want to chat up those handsome men!"

Paddy's flippancy and glibness undermined Margery's confidence. She hated herself for being petty, but she felt that Paddy had stolen her brother, her mother, her home and herself – her better self.

England, March 1943

The telephone rang and Paddy rushed to answer it. She loved to gossip, taking a chair into the hall and spending hours wrapped in a rug talking to her girlfriends.

"It's for you, Curly, the ever faithful Donald," she said loudly as she held the receiver towards Margery.

Bother Paddy, Margery thought; he must have heard that.

"Hello Donald. How nice to hear from you! Are you home for a few days?"

"Yes, Margery. I've got a bit of leave. I wondered whether you'd care to pop up to London with me one evening?"

"Oh Donald, that would be a real treat. What did you have in mind?"

"Well, I've got a chum who can wangle me a couple of tickets for *Blithe Spirit*, you know, the Noel Coward play, and then I thought we might go to a London club, Quaggalinos perhaps, and catch the last train home. How does that sound?"

"Top notch. When are you thinking of going?"

"Next Tuesday perhaps. Are you free?"

"Yes, I'm off duty that day but back on mornings on Wednesday."

"I have to get back to base on Wednesday too. I'll pick you up about 4 o'clock."

"Lovely Donald. I'll look forward to it." Margery replaced the phone and smiled to herself. She felt like a child promised a trip to the sea. She walked back into the kitchen.

"What did he want, Curly?"

"He wants to take me out."

"To the Hen and Chicks for a pie and a pint?" Paddy sneered as she blew a smoke ring.

"No, up to Town to see *Blithe Spirit* and dancing at Quaggalinos, afterwards." Paddy's jaw dropped; Margery knew she had never been to Quaggalinos.

"He must be keen on you, Curly. He's a real catch, an only son with a thriving business to inherit. What will Brian think if you give him the push for Donald?"

Margery bent to stroke Judy. She wasn't going to rise to that remark. With no response, Paddy turned to the serious business.

"What are you going to wear?"

Margery had no spare coupons; she'd have to wear something she already had.

"Let's go and look," said Paddy. Margery was taller than Paddy but Paddy had the fuller figure; she had some lovely evening clothes that she would lend to Margery to complete an outfit. The two girls went down the hall to Margery's bedroom. Paddy opened the wardrobe door and took out three possible dresses, then she went to her own room and came back with two more.

"Try them on, Curly." Margery put on frock after frock and Paddy put her head on one side to consider. Her small bedroom was littered with discarded dresses, drifting as deep as leaves in autumn. Paddy had good taste and was a stylish dresser; Margery had always been more conservative. It was fun with Paddy as her fashion guru. Perhaps there were some advantages in having a sister-in-law.

Margery decided to wear the frock she had worn to Paddy's wedding, an evening cloak borrowed from Paddy, her only pair of high heeled shoes and her precious silk stockings bought on the black market.

Margery was ready when Donald arrived, dressed in his dinner jacket with a white scarf thrown casually around his neck. He held Paddy's evening cloak while Margery put it on.

"Let's go and say 'Goodbye' to Johnnie," said Margery. "He's home on sick leave with another bout of bronchitis." They went into the sitting room and parted the dividing curtain. Johnnie was lying on the sofa beside the fire with a rug over his knees.

"I won't get up, old chap, but it's good to see you. We must get together sometime for a pint." A bout of coughing stopped Johnnie.

"Yes, next time I'm home, perhaps. Sorry you've been poorly."

"This wretched chest of mine has been playing up a bit."

"Wow, you look such a lovely couple. Don't do anything I wouldn't do." Paddy was sitting sideways on the sofa holding Johnnie's hand. She waved them off as they left in Donald's car.

"Johnnie doesn't look too good, does he?"

"No, but he is recovering now. He should be all right again in a week or two the doctor says."

"It must be a worry for you all."

"Mum's very worried and so is Pad. It's hard to see where it's going."

"I suppose so. Have you heard from Brian lately?"

"Yes, his new camp is by a river with woods coming down to the wire. They can't go out of course but he likes to see the trees." Margery hesitated and sighed; Donald glanced at her.

"What is it Margery? You sound worried."

"It's this handcuffing thing. He's in chains and I'm worried he'll be deformed, you know twisted or something, having to keep his hands like that all the time."

"It's brutal, that. These wretched Huns! Lots of my chums are in the bag too. Brian is young and fit; I'm sure he'll be all right." Margery put her cares aside. She wanted to enjoy herself tonight; Brian would like that.

The play was lively, Margery loved dancing at the 'posh' London nightclub and, tired but happy, they caught the last train back. But the train was delayed by troop movements;

they always took priority on the line. When they finally reached Woking Station Donald looked for the taxi that he had booked to meet them.

"I don't know where he's got to," said Donald. "Perhaps we'd better have a look around the other side." They walked through the underpass, their footsteps echoing on the tiled walls, but there was still no car. Donald looked at his watch.

"He's usually so reliable," he said. "I'm sorry about this, Margery."

"I think he must have given up as we're so late. Perhaps we'd better walk to your house," she said.

"It's a couple of miles. Are you sure?"

"Yes but look the other way while I take off my stockings. I can't afford to ladder them." Donald obliged and they set off along the lanes in the blackout.

"When we get to my place, I can get my car and run you home. It's past two o'clock. I hope your mother won't be worried."

"Don't worry. She'll be fast asleep and snoring but I'm on duty at eight tomorrow."

"You work hard, don't you? I don't know any other girls who take their war work so seriously."

"I enjoy the hospital, and I always wanted to be a nurse."

When they arrived at Stone Cottage, Donald walked her up to the door.

"I'm back to my squadron tomorrow and it'll be a few weeks before I'm home again. But I'll look you up."

"Good night, it's been a lovely evening. Thank you so much." She gave him a quick kiss on his cheek as she turned to go into the kitchen.

England, April 1943

Margery was walking down the hall as the phone rang. I'll get there before Paddy this time, she thought.

"Brookwood 2323"

"Is that you, Margery? It's Alice here, Donald's mother."

"Hello, how nice to hear from you."

"I'm ringing about Donald, my dear. I thought I should tell you that his plane didn't come back yesterday morning. He's missing."

Margery felt a lead weight drop on her stomach. She didn't know what to say; there were no words.

"His friends say that his plane was hit and they saw it losing height. He might have been able to bale out but... they didn't know."

"I'm so sorry. That's a dreadful blow."

"You and he have been such good friends recently and we thought you ought to know before we put it in the papers."

"Yes, many thanks for telling me. It is a shock. Is there anything I can do?"

"Just pray," said Alice.

Margery thought of all the people she'd prayed for – Brian, Johnnie, Andrew and now Donald – God must be working overtime, looking after our boys and the Germans too.

"Please let me know if there's any more news," she said.

"Of course, Margery. Goodbye."

Margery put the receiver back on its hook and walked

back to her bedroom, stunned. The tears were running down her cheeks. This was too much, far too much. Would this wretched war ever stop? It was taking such a toll on the young men, the boys she'd laughed with, danced with, flirted with. The Great War had lasted four years but this one had been going nearly as long as that and seemed set to continue forever.

England, 2016

We sat in the garden at the care home, the tall pine trees casting welcome shade. My mother liked to be taken outside; she was ever the gardener. The geraniums spilled over the herbaceous beds like blue beads.

"Look, Mum. It's Geranium Suzanne."

With her fading sight she peered from her wheelchair.

"It could have been Margery," she said. One of the carers was with us. She looked nonplussed; she probably thought Mum was confused. But I knew. We had been over this ground before.

It had all started a few years before on a trip to a show garden. I pushed her around the grounds, resplendent in the summer sunshine. She came from a family of nursery men; rhododendrons and azaleas were their speciality and, although we were too late for those, the herbaceous beds were impressive.

"Go and have a look at that label," said my mother, pointing her walking stick at a rambling display of violet blue geraniums. I did as I was told.

"It says Geranium Susanne, Mum."

"I thought so. Donald bred it and named it for his wife."

I knew the family; they had been our friends. I had played, bickered, danced and flirted with their son, Tom, a handsome young man. But there was something not quite right here.

"Donald? I thought he bred rhododendrons and azaleas like Uncle Johnnie."

"He did, but he bred this geranium too." She sounded so sure, so certain, yet it didn't ring true. Was she getting muddled? Was this some story she had dreamt up? After all she had lived so long; it must be hard to remember.

"Didn't Suzanne spell her name with a Z?" I said.

"Yes, of course, she did." My mother dismissed my question, as if she were swatting away a fly.

"Well, the label spells Susanne with an S."

"They've got it wrong." She had never been big on patience and the little she had had was wearing thin after 90 years.

I kept quiet but it didn't sound likely. This was a flagship garden; they wouldn't make a mistake, would they? I took the brake off the wheelchair and moved on.

Four years later there was a national plant competition, the winner to be decided by public ballot. Geranium Suzanne – spelt with a Z – won the award. I took the press cuttings to my mother; Donald and his wife beamed from the page holding the plant aloft.

"He was my insurance policy, you know. He would have married me if Dad hadn't come back and then it would have been Geranium Margery."

"You could have been immortalised as a geranium, Mum."

CHAPTER 24

Eichstätt, Spring 1943

As the ground dried up and the sports season arrived, Brian was annoyed to find he could only play hockey; with his chains, rugger and football were beyond him. Sports matches passed the time, those endless acres of time stretching ahead until the Allies won the war. The *Kriegies* had an illicit radio nicknamed 'Jimmy' and at 9pm every evening one officer from each block listened to the BBC news. After lights out, the whispers would go around:

"Jimmy says Mussolini's wavering and old Adolf's trying to gee him up."

"Jimmy says we've taken Tunis."

"Jimmy says we're going to invade Sicily."

The Allies were making progress but it seemed painfully slow, like building a wall one pebble at a time and Brian was impatient. He ran his hand along the table, feeling the grooves in the rough wood as he read Margery's latest letter. Her letters came regularly, and each one seemed to tell of change; their friends from before the war were lost, gone, scattered. Johnnie was married, a whirlwind romance with his childhood playmate, Paddy Jones. Fleda had let her house and gone to Birmingham to drive an Army lorry. Phyllis had joined the Land Army, whatever that was, and Donald was reported 'missing over Germany'. Brian thought of those RAF chaps in Warburg and their tales of escaping from burning aircraft, travelling in secret across Germany. Being a *Kriegie* was not something he'd wish on anyone, not even Donald, but, as it was infinitely better than the alternative, he hoped Donald had been captured.

The warmer weather meant the *Kriegies* spent more time out of doors and the sunlight, the warmth and the change of company raised Brian's spirits. He wished the Goons would remove the shackles.

"They can't do it, old boy," said Elliot. "Hitler's orders; but Blätters is looking into altering the design." A week later the shackles were changed.

"These new handcuffs are more convenient," said Bill. "I've got about two feet of chain now."

"Yes, they're much better. I do believe the Goons are getting soft." A subtle change was in the air and the atmosphere in the camp felt lighter. Brian was setting out some tomato plants when Bob wandered over, his hands in his pockets.

"It looks as if you could do with a bit more soil around those plants." He winked at Brian.

"It wouldn't come amiss, old boy. I suppose it's Jock's tunnel, is it?"

"Yes, they're nearly there."

In early June, Jock's tunnel broke in a chicken coop beyond the wire and 65 officers got out. This was the largest escape to date and Brian was jubilant. Blätters was furious, of course.

"Theatre *verboten,* football *verboten* and mail *verboten*," he announced at *Appell*. The ban on mail hit Brian particularly hard; he missed Margery's letters, missed reading her words, smelling her perfume, placing his fingers were hers had been. The letters were their bond, the links in the chain joining them together.

"Bother these escapers!" he said to Bill.

"Just think though, all those Goons, policemen and Hitler Youth members out there hunting for his gang." Bill winked and Brian had to agree.

Escapes infuriated Blätters; he strutted around barking out orders like a tin-pot dictator and seemed to relish reading out the punishment orders at *Appell*.

'Lieutenant Roberts: Awarded 5 days because on morning parade he is late and in bed.'

'Captain Powell: Awarded 5 days for undisciplined behaviour on morning parade, blowing his nose in a provoking manner.'

'Lieutenant Wheeler: Awarded 5 days for undisciplined behaviour on morning parade. He sat on a stool to read while all is standing to attention.'

"He sure gets mad at us," said Bud as they walked back to Block 1.

"Yeah, *Appell* lasted two hours yesterday."

"You know what? I hear he's the only guy in the camp who hasn't seen active service."

"Really," said Brian, raising his eyebrows. "That might explain it. He's got something to prove."

Blätters was obsessed with the officers' appearance. After three years in captivity, their uniforms were tatty and some of them didn't care; they didn't sew on lost buttons, didn't repair split seams, didn't bother about frayed trouser cuffs. No-one was going to see them – except the Goons and they didn't matter.

"He's like a bloody prefect," said Brian. "*Verboten* to leave one's jacket unbuttoned, *verboten* to come to *Appell* without full uniform, *verboten* to read books at *Appell*. He's obsessed with that word."

"These rules sure make my head spin," said Bud. They were in a vortex. The more Blätters blustered, the scruffier the *Kriegies* became; the longer *Appell* lasted, the more books and notepads the *Kriegies* brought with them. Blätters bellowed but the *Kriegies* ignored him; he couldn't send them all to the cooler. They seemed to have reached an impasse.

One morning, the officers looked particularly slovenly and Blätters berated them for an hour in German. He gave them the full works, uniforms, shirts, boots, caps and jackets. Brian picked up the gist of it.

"It is forbidden to attend *Appell* without wearing a shirt," came the translation. A ripple of interest ran through the ranks of officers. This could be fun.

"We must obey, of course," said the SBO and the word went around the camp, whispered from man to man, from room to room, from block to block until everyone was in on the secret – except the Goons. As Brian left his room the following morning, he looked Bill up and down.

"I see you're wearing your shirt, old chap."

"Of course, it's orders."

As the *Kriegies* lined up, Brian looked along the rows, at Bud, at Bill, at Elliot, at Bob; they were all wearing shirts. Blätters strutted out, the sunlight glinting off the golden eagle on his cap. The order rang out for the officers to come to attention and Brian stamped his feet together. Six thousand boots struck the parade ground like a thunderclap. The Goons looked, looked again and tittered. Blätters looked and started; his face and neck reddened like a cockerel preparing to fight, then he turned on his heel and left the parade ground. Each and every officer was standing to attention wearing a shirt… but nothing else.

After that life in the camp became easier. The spring turned into summer, the tomato plants began to fruit and the rumours kept going, stronger than ever.

"They say the Goons will exchange prisoners…"

"I heard that the *Kriegies* who've been here more than three years are going to Switzerland…"

"You know the sick and wounded are being sent home…"

That one was true and Brian watched the officers climb into the trucks.

"Don't you wish you were going with them?" said Bob, as the convoy left the camp.

"I wish I was going, but I'm glad I've got my health. It's a great blessing even if we have to wait a bit longer."

Eichstätt, Autumn 1943

"Jimmy says Mussolini's surrendered…"

"We'll be home by Christmas…" They said that every Christmas. Although Brian was still in shackles, camp life had improved.

"The Goons are getting worried," said Elliot. "When we win the war, we'll be the ones holding the War Crimes' Tribunals."

Brian nodded as he darned a sock, a difficult task in chains. Elliot certainly knew what he was talking about and, at the next *Appell*, Blätters announced new privileges: parole walks, cinema visits and permission to publish a camp magazine.

A rota was drawn up for the parole walks and Brian

noted that his name was way down the list. He watched as, twice a week, a party of *Kriegies* went out through the gates and into the woods. It made such a difference to walk beyond the wire, to see their valley from a different angle, to smell the scents in the woodland; these simple pleasures were a real delight.

"It's just grand to feel the pine needles underfoot." Bob's eyes shone as he came back. "I've brought some wood for the stove."

"I loved the view as we went through the birch trees and looked along the valley," said Bill to Brian who longed to see beyond those birch trees. "There were some juicy blackberries in the hedge and I picked some for tea."

"It sure is great to get outside the gates," said Bud. "A guy can breathe easy on the outside."

Brian dreamed, imagining the pleasures in store for him, like a kid before his birthday. At the end of October he lay in his bunk drifting between sleeping and waking, considering the day ahead; same old people, same old routine, but then he remembered. Today was special, the day for his walk, his first walk in the woods beyond the wire. What a treat! He peered through the tiny window to look at the weather; they only went if it was fine. Sun shone down on the parade ground, lifting its ugliness and Brian's spirits.

His heart thumped as he walked through the gates; he hadn't been outside the camp since he arrived over a year ago. He strolled with the others into the beech woods, those woods with their ever-changing light and shade, with the scent of fresh, damp earth and the twigs crackling underfoot; he savoured every moment. He saw the blackbird flitting from branch to branch, he noticed the cobwebs glistening with dew, he heard the wind whistling in the branches. He stored it all in his memory. I will be able to relive these joys when I'm back in camp, he thought, and I will have something new to tell Margery. I'll never again underrate the simple things in life.

Then came the day they had all been waiting for, the day they were released from their shackles. The Goons unharnessed the *Kriegies* and took the shackles to their storeroom.

"Isn't it grand," said Bill. "I can stretch my arms at last and we can mix freely with the others."

That made a real difference; Brian could visit Bob whenever he wanted. They no longer depended on chance meetings on the parade ground. Then Elliot came to see him.

"Brian, there's someone I'd like you to meet. He's a chartered accountant and I think he'll be prepared to tutor you."

"That sounds promising. Who is he?"

"A Scot named Rob," said Elliot. "He was captured in Tunisia. I might be able to wangle it so you get moved into the same room."

That was a real stroke of luck. Rob was the same age as Brian, a quietly mannered man from Beith in Scotland, a good team player, and a nature lover; he agreed to tutor Brian. When the time came to sit his exams once again, Brian felt confident.

"I'll pass them this time, Rob, I'm sure. You've made all the difference." And he did. Success in both

Accountancy and English.

"Well done, Brian," said Elliot, shaking his hand.

"Thanks, Elliot, but just between you, me and the gatepost, I think they only let me through the English so that the Goons wouldn't have a laugh at a British officer failing his English Language."

"It doesn't matter, old chap, you've passed."

Eichstätt, Winter 1944

The New Year brought the pantomime season and the camp players produced *Dossing Dulcie*, an adaptation – a very loose adaptation – of *Sleeping Beauty*. The whole camp bought tickets for this annual event and Brian went to watch with Bob and Rob; it was Rob's first pantomime.

"I loved the moral and the immoral fairies," said Bob, winking. It had been amusing to see their fellow *Kriegies* dressed in tutus, their legs shaved, their bodices stuffed with old socks. They were the fairies, simpering over the cradle at Dulcie's christening.

"Yes, I found the script very witty," said Rob. "Lots of local references worked into the traditional tale."

"They usually do us proud," said Brian. "I think we're quite a critical audience; we live in such a narrow world that we pour over every word. The panto becomes a major topic of conversation as there's not much else to talk about. How do you think it compares with last year, Bob?"

"Oh better, I think. In fact, I think the standard's been going up year on year."

"It's only right that the last should be the best," Brian said and this year he meant it. The Allies were making gains in Italy and in Eastern Europe and there were whispers about opening a Western Front. The air raids were unremitting. One evening Brian and Rob were standing in the darkness hearing the throbbing engines as the RAF planes went over.

"Where do you think they're headed?" asked Rob as the drumming faded away.

"Munich, probably. Jimmy says the Allies are bombing heavily to weaken the morale of the German people."

"Poor sods!" Rob shook his head. "It won't do much good, though, while Hitler's still in power."

"I think the end will come this year," said Brian, "one way or another. That's why I'm not knitting. I'm too slow and we'll be home by next winter, I'm sure."

Knitting was the new craze. The *Kriegies* whittled needles from sticks, unravelled wool from old socks and knitted jumpers to keep them warm in the Bavarian winter.

"I'm thinking about what it will be like to get home. It's four years now since I was in England." Brian lit another cigarette.

"Whew, that's a long time. You must feel a bit out of touch."

"Yes, I've been trying to work out my finances but there's so many unknowns. I've been saving, of course, while I'm here." Brian's captain's pay had been going into his bank account and he had totted up how much was there, added that to his pre-war savings and he reckoned there should be a nice little nest egg. "When I marry, there's going to be a hell of a lot of expense, a honeymoon, setting up house and so on and I'm out of touch with prices now."

"Well, they're certainly not going down, old boy, that's

for sure. I tell you what, I've been thinking of a little wheeze that might make us both a bob or two."

"What's that then?"

"Well, you know the *Kriegies* love a flutter? They'll bet on anything?" Brian did know; he'd watched his roommates lay bets on which raindrop would reach the windowsill first, or whether that blackbird sitting on the wire would fly into the camp or outside to freedom.

"Suppose you and I set up as bookies? We've got the expertise; I'll work out the odds while you handle the cash and keep the records. We'll make out betting slips and sign them to make it official. What do you say?"

"Would we stick to matches, you know the football and rugger matches, or would we open a book on anything, like which fly will be the first to land on my dinner plate?" Brian stroked his moustache as he considered Rob's idea.

"Oh, anything, I think, as long as there's more than one possible outcome. We'll keep the field as wide as possible and we can't go wrong, can we?" Rob winked at Brian.

"Right-ho." Brian smiled. "I'll give it a whirl. It might pay for my honeymoon and Margery will be tickled pink. I'll have to keep quiet to my parents, though; my mother thinks gambling, cards, alcohol and chocolate are the Devil's work."

Brian and Rob were well respected amongst the *Kriegies.* Brian's quiet demeanour and stoicism had earned him a wide circle of acquaintance while Rob's sporting prowess was prized. The accountant and the banker never lacked punters.

"What are the odds on Block 3 for the football tournament?" asked Bill. Brian took his book out of his pocket and consulted his notes.

"Six to four for a win, or three to one for a draw."

"All right, that'll do me." Bill paid his stake and pocketed the betting slip that Brian signed. When Bill came back on Saturday afternoon to redeem his winnings, Brian screwed up his eyes and checked the slip, the amount, the odds and his signature. It's like the bank, he thought; you can't be too careful where money's concerned. Bill's slip passed his scrutiny and he paid out.

"Brian, have you got a book on the war?" asked John. "You know who will win and when?"

"We've got a book on when it will end, but we don't take bets on *who* will win; that's not cricket." For British officers only one outcome was admissible.

"No, of course not, old man. I was thinking that the Allies must be about to open a Western Front and that it will all be over by Christmas."

"Yes, I can give you odds on that," said Brian. John placed his bet and Brian signed the betting slip. 'All over by Christmas' was a popular option. Bud, however, had other ideas.

"It seems to me that the Yanks are a bit slow getting going," he said. Bud rubbed his crew cut and looked thoughtful. "But they won't want the Ruskies to get all the credit for winning the war. They'll have to get a move on, I reckon. What are the odds on the end coming in May 1945?"

Brian gave him long odds, took his money and made out a betting slip. This was turning out to be a nice little earner. He would be able to afford a good honeymoon.

England and Canada, 1975

"The bank wants you to go to Canada to set up a new business," the Board said. "You're just the man for the job."

In his pinstripe suit, with the bottom button on his waistcoat left undone, my father typified the British banker; for him the motto 'My Word is My Bond' meant what it said. He was a safe pair of hands, good at developing contacts and shrewd at assessing risk. He'd always been the bank's loyal servant so he had no doubts. This was his chance to see those lakes, those forests, those open prairies that he had heard so much about in Eichstätt. But my mother was apprehensive.

"What about the journey?" She had never been on an aeroplane.

"It'll be fine."

"What about the children?"

"They're old enough to live their own lives."

"What about the house?"

"We'll let it. The bank will help us to buy in Toronto." He swept aside her misgivings, they packed up and off they went.

"That's strange," my father said, as he opened the post one morning in Toronto. "My attorney wants me to go to a meeting with the vendor about the house purchase. I didn't think they liked the two parties to get together over this side of the Atlantic."

"I hope nothing's wrong. That house is just perfect. It's big enough for visitors but not too big when it's just us. It's even got a small garden to keep me busy."

"I'm sure it'll all be fine. I'll give the attorney a ring and see what it's about."

But he didn't know. The searches were done, the papers were signed and they had been sent to the vendor's attorney. All was in order; and then came this unusual request for a meeting.

Puzzled, Brian rode up to the tenth floor in the elevator and walked into the attorney's office. He saw the lake shining below and he noticed a man sitting at the table looking out of the window. He rose and turned towards my father.

"Do you remember me, Brian?" He came forward, holding out his hand. "When I saw your signature on those papers, it was like I was back in Oflag VIIB. I asked my attorney 'Who is this guy?' When he told me you were British, I said: 'I just gotta meet him'. It sure is a small world."

"Bud, after all these years. Well, what a surprise! You had me worried, you know."

"It's all fine with the house, Brian, just fine. This is what I've come about." Bud drew a small slip of paper out of his pocket. "I got it right, didn't I? Jerry surrendered in May 1945 but we'd been liberated by then so you never paid me. I thought I'd call in the debt."

CHAPTER 25

England, September 1943

"Aren't they sweet, Mum?" said John. At nine years old, he was no longer little John and he was ecstatic about Judy's puppies, little black bundles with spaniel ears but bull terrier faces. The dirty window admitted a dim light and cobwebs hung in the corners of the garage, where Judy had her nursery. She watched as their unsteady legs weaved across the floor like drunks at a party. The puppies were a mistake, Paddy's mistake; she had left the door open when Judy was in season and, by the time Judy was found, the deed had been done and these eight little bundles of mischief were the result. Judy was a proud mother.

"Can I pick one up, please?" John asked.

"Yes, of course you can. Judy doesn't mind. Let me show you how." Margery supported the pup under its tummy, cupped her hand over the velvet fur of its back, noticing the sweet smell of milk, as she passed it to John.

"It's so warm and cuddly." He held it up to his neck. "Can I have one please, Mum? We could keep it in the garage as Father's allergic and I promise I'd take it for walks. Please, Mum, please." Doris shook her head.

"You know it's out of the question. Your father would never allow it. And besides he wants you to go to boarding school soon."

John looked crestfallen and Margery felt sorry for him. Judy was such a comfort to her. A pet-free home was empty, a mere shell; no dog to take for walks, to greet you when you came home, to lick your hand when you felt troubled. She didn't want her children to grow up like that.

"I tell you what. You can stay here in the garage and play with the puppies for a bit. Then after lunch I'll take you for a ride on Joey."

John perked up and dangled a piece of old sock at the puppies. They pounced and he tugged as Margery and Doris stepped out, closing the door behind them.

"Have you got homes for them all?"

"Nearly, the bitches are all taken but two of the boys are not spoken for yet. One of Pad's sisters is interested and a nurse at the hospital thinks her mum might have one. It's a shame John can't have a dog and what's all this about boarding school?"

"Hether thinks it would be good for him as he's an only child."

Margery knew Doris would have loved another baby, a little girl perhaps like Brenda's Rosemary. "I suppose he'll have to go eventually, after he takes his Common Entrance. But I'd like to keep him home for a few more years. He's doing well at his day school."

Margery nodded. She hadn't thought about children's schooling. Would she and Brian send their children to boarding school? Money was bound to be tight when they set up home and they might not be able to afford it. The government wanted to introduce a welfare system and she could see the sense in that; some of her patients lived in dreadful conditions, no bathroom, no shoes for their children, no money for a doctor. On the other hand, though, welfare had to be paid for and she worried about how the taxes would affect young couples like her and Brian.

"Hello, Doris," said Nellie as they came into the

kitchen. "I'm pleased you could get over for lunch. We miss having you to stay these days but we've got no space now Paddy is with us. By the way, she's feeling a bit peaky today so she's going to stay in her room."

"Oh poor Paddy!"

"Is she poorly *again*, Mum?" Margery felt Paddy was putting it on; ever since she came back from her honeymoon, she'd been fussing. "I thought she was better yesterday afternoon."

"Yes, but she was bad again this morning. She felt queasy and she was sick, poor thing."

"Was she now?" Doris looked meaningfully at Nellie.

"Maybe, maybe, it's too early to tell for sure," Nellie said.

Margery's head spun; she felt as if she had been knocked over. Was that why Nellie was being so solicitous, bringing Paddy sips of boiled water and fingers of dry toast? Was Paddy going to produce the first Street grandchild? It wasn't fair; she'd waited so long.

"I expect your mother's pleased to have Brenda at home," Nellie said.

"She loves it but she finds it tiring. Rosemary's very good but all babies cry a bit. Then there's the washing; nappies take so long to dry."

Nellie nodded. Margery thought Stone Cottage would be a tight squeeze if Paddy had a baby; the walls were paper thin and the rooms so small.

"Tell me the latest about Brian," said Doris. "Daddy heard some story about the prisoners going for walks. Is there any truth in that?"

"Yes, it's true all right; he's waiting for his turn to come round. But he's still in chains. It's been nearly a year now. It must be dreadful for him."

"He's quite resilient, my little brother. He'll be all right you'll see." Doris gave Margery a quick hug. "Mummy's getting worried about Bernard. He might have to go soon and she can't bear the idea. I'm glad John's too young." Just at that moment, John came bursting in.

"Auntie Margery, one of the puppies has done a wee on the floor."

"Oh dear! It can't be helped; I'll clear it up later. I hope you shut the garage door when you came out. We don't want the puppies to escape."

"I'll just go back and make sure," he said.

"And then, John, you'd better go and wash your hands ready for lunch."

England, January 1944

Margery drove to work for her night shift. She stopped in Chobham to pick up Chris; her petrol rations depended on passengers. Margery creased her eyes as she peered through the windscreen; the blackout left the roads inky dark, like the inside of a cave;

"What have you been up to today?" Chris said.

"I slept for a few hours this morning and then I went shopping with Paddy this afternoon."

"That must have been fun."

"It was. We ran into a couple of ex-patients, some of those Canadians we had in last summer. They wanted us to go and have a drink with them. Paddy was impressed that I knew so many handsome men."

"I'll bet she was. She's always been such a flirt."

"She still is even with a baby on the way. She's says she's going to write to Brian and tell him all about my 'other boyfriends', as she calls them."

"Will he mind?"

"No, not a bit. He knows what Paddy's like. She doesn't get the hang of it. At the hospital it's a conveyor belt; we've always got men coming in, getting better and going off. I've met lots of soldiers but most of them don't stick around for long. It's the war, I suppose. Here we are Chris. I'll see you in the morning."

Night Sister was not there when Margery arrived on the ward. That's odd, she thought; Fanny Morris is a stickler for punctuality. She stood in front of the desk, her hands behind her back while Fanny Clark, the Day Sister, looked at her through her glasses.

"Nurse Street, I am glad you're on duty tonight. Sister Morris has got 'flu and is running a temperature. I have talked to Matron and you're to take charge tonight."

"Sister, I'm only a VAD," Margery gawped.

"I know but you have four years' experience and the ward's under control. If anything crops up that you feel you can't handle, phone Sister Adams on Men's Surgical. Now we'll go through the handover."

"Yes, Sister." Margery listened carefully as Sister ran through each patient, explaining the ones who might need more drugs.

"Nurse Street, you have my full confidence."

Margery's heart hammered and she felt an imposter as Fanny Clark swept out of the ward. Nurse Dabbs was also on duty. She came from Wales, a farmer's daughter, who had married a local lad. Margery remembered the midnight party at Christmas when Nurse Dabbs had brought some flat little scones made with real butter from her parents' cows – Welsh cakes she called them; they had melted in the mouth.

Margery went on her rounds. The patients were settling for the night, turning and twisting to get comfy. The ward looked in perfect order. When the last pillow had been thumped, the last bandage adjusted and the last glass of water drunk, the overhead lights were turned out. The lamp on Sister's desk cast a soft pool of light and Margery started to relax. Nurse Dabbs sat beside her, knitting the sleeve for a sweater.

"It's for my husband. He's away with his regiment in Italy."

Margery told her about Brian and their long-delayed wedding. All was quiet when Nurse Dabbs went for her lunch break and Margery walked round her ward like a groom patrolling the stables. Everyone was asleep so she started to write to Brian about everyday things like shopping for shoes, playing pat-a-cake with Rosemary and young John's new-found delight in rugger. She heard the clock ticking, the patients snoring and the distant clank of doors shutting.

The patient in Bed 6 tossed and groaned and his iron bedstead creaked; she'd better see to him before he woke the others. She tiptoed along, her torch painting a streak of yellow across the shadows.

"My leg's giving me gyp, Nurse."

Margery took his pulse, temperature and blood pressure. Then she checked the traction on his broken leg. She went through her routine like the practiced steps of a dance.

Everything was in order so she gave him a sedative and went back to her desk to write up the notes. When she looked up, he had fallen asleep and she sighed with relief; she might be only a VAD but she could take responsibility for the ward.

England, June 1944

The Reverend Smythe intoned the words of the Christening Service and Margery watched as Frank Dowling held the baby. Brian was godfather to Johnnie's child and, in his absence, his father was standing proxy.

"Frederick Andrew, I baptise thee in the name of the Father and of the Son and of the Holy Ghost."

Andrew yelled as the holy water was poured over his head, drenching the fine lace christening gown. Margery smiled at Nellie who whispered: "Perhaps we'll have some peace tonight if he yells all afternoon."

Margery looked at the group standing by the font and then her eyes strayed around the church; she noted the flowers on the altar, the commemoration plaques, the dust motes dancing in the sun and she wondered how long it would be until she stood by the altar rail with Brian. Her wedding was already four years late; surely it wouldn't be much longer?

At the reception, Margery passed round tea and christening cake. She came to Frank and Amy, standing a little apart from the other guests. Amy looked drained, as if it was too much effort to mingle and Frank stood with her.

"It was good of you, Dad, to stand proxy for Brian."

"I was glad to, my dear, but it's quite a responsibility

renouncing the Devil and all his works for that little bundle. Now tell me, about his name. Frederick I can understand, after your Uncle Fred, but why Andrew?"

"It's for Johnnie's friend who was killed in that dreadful accident a few years ago."

"Ah yes, my dear. I'd forgotten his name. So many fine young men have been lost in this war. It won't go on much longer now, I'm sure of it."

"It does seem more hopeful after D-Day. We've had a lot of casualties coming into the hospital. It's as busy as it was at the time of Dunkirk."

"You work too hard, my dear." Amy sniffed and Margery smiled at her but didn't respond; she knew better now.

"Johnnie says it's the last push. He thinks the Germans will surrender soon and Brian will come home for Christmas." Margery looked at Frank and his eyes twinkled through his glasses.

"I pray for it, my dear, every day." Frank put his hand on her arm.

"Have you thought about how long you might wait before you get married?" asked Amy. I'm not having her interfering, thought Margery; it's our decision. She smiled at Amy.

"Why yes, Mum. How funny that you should mention it. Brian and I have been talking about that in our letters and we've decided that, once he's home, we're not going to wait any longer. It's been over four years already."

"We think Brian might need some time to settle," said Amy, pursing her lips and looking at Frank.

"So much has changed, my dear, since he went away,"

said Frank. "New babies, new standards and new ideas. Take this Education Bill for example; free secondary schooling for everyone is going to make a difference and then there's this Welfare State. It's a new country he's coming back to."

"Yes, you're right. He will need to adjust and we've talked about that. *We* think that he will settle best with me by his side," said Margery. Frank nodded but Amy buttoned her mouth into a tight little knot. Brenda came over, leading Rosemary by the hand, her dark curls shining. She tottered up to Margery and tugged at the hem of her frock.

"Margy, Margy."

Margery bent to lift her godchild in her arms. She longed for a baby of her own, a cousin for Rosemary and Andrew. Once we're married, she thought, I want to start a family. She felt like a child waiting for the playground slide; everyone else's turn came before hers. Margery carried Rosemary towards the kitchen and Judy thumped her tail but she didn't move from her bed.

"Doggie, doggie," said Rosemary. Margery put her on the floor and held her little hand as she stroked Judy's ears, soft and silky as only spaniels' ears could be. Margery ran her hand down Judy's side, noticing her ribs.

"Poor girl, you never really got over those puppies, did you? You look like I feel at the end of a shift." Judy thumped her tail again and followed Margery with her eyes as she took Rosemary back to the party.

CHAPTER 26

Eichstätt, Spring 1944

Tension hung in the air; Brian knew, Bob knew, all the *Kriegies* knew and even the Goons knew what was coming. Rumours flew around the camp and every evening Brian asked the chap who listened to Jimmy: "Has it happened?"

"Nothing yet," came the reply, day after day, week after week. On the 28th of May, Brian and the others from the Bucks Battalion commemorated the fourth anniversary of their capture and still there was no news. Then, on the 6th of June, Jimmy reported Operation Overlord, the D-Day landings, and the camp erupted.

"Hurrah, hurrah!"

"A Western Front, at last."

"We really will be home by Christmas."

They all agreed that liberation must come soon; the military implications were clear. The personal implications were harder as each man was differently placed.

"It'll be a bit of a grind, going back to the accounts office," Rob said.

"I've never had a job in civvy street," said John.

Brian remembered that he'd been up at Oxford reading Philosophy when the war broke out. Brian knew he could go back to the bank. They'd promised him a job and, with his exams behind him, it should pay enough to support a quiet life with Margery. The bank routine – counting the money, cashing up, making the books balance – appealed to him now; he had had enough of adventure to last a lifetime.

"It's those damned whippersnappers," said Tom. "I

taught them how to salute when the war started but now they've been promoted over me. It really takes the biscuit."

Brian considered this and realised that he would need to see what the bank would offer in terms of salary and seniority. He had been away five years, commanded a company and passed his exams; he wouldn't want to go back as a junior clerk.

"My girl's going to grammar school this year," said Pop. "She'd only just started in kindergarten when I saw her last."

Brian thought of little John and of Bernard's boy. They'd both be at prep school now and there were all these 'war babies', born since he left: Jean's two boys, Bernard's little girl, Brenda's infant, and Johnnie's baby son. So many new people; he must try and get the hang of who would be crawling, walking, talking and so on.

"What about Norah?" he asked Bob. The flat green leaves of the lime trees were shading the parade ground, as they walked around with Rob. "Do you think you'll get married straightaway?"

"We'll probably wait a bit to get to know each other again. Five years is a long time."

"We're both lucky our girls have waited for us." Brian knew that last week a man, jilted by his fiancée, had run for the wire but he hadn't been shot, he'd been taken to the hospital; the Goons were wary now the war was going against them.

"It's easy for you, Rob. You haven't got big decisions to make."

"That's true, but Bridget and I can't just pick up where we left off. We've got an infant now; she's got the cot in the bedroom, for feeding and that, but I've never seen him and I think it'll take me a while to get the hang of being a father."

Brian pondered this. He had always thought of Margery as his, his sweetheart, his companion, his fiancée. What would it be like to share her with an infant?

"I never thought of that. I suppose Margery and I do have a clean slate."

"That's it exactly, old man."

"You know we're going to have to think about tidying ourselves up ready for home – our language, our habits and so on."

"Mmm," said Bob, smiling, "especially Phil, the Great Unwashed!"

Phil spent all day in pyjamas and rarely went to the bathhouse. Brian and Bob had found in those dreadful days in Laufen that a daily routine provided a structure, like lines in a colouring book; Brian felt he was more than just *Kriegsgefangener 765* when he was clean and tidy.

"There's all that camp slang too; it's not much good going home, if no-one is able to understand a word we're saying." They grinned at each other, glad at last to be working towards their liberation.

A spell of good weather brought new privileges, more walks, cinema visits and bathing parties in the river. Brian loved swimming and his turn was pure delight. As he lay on the riverbank, sunning himself, he remembered the summer holidays with Johnnie and Margery at Sandbanks when they swam before breakfast. Nellie provided a good spread after a swim; bacon, eggs, fried bread, mushrooms and as much toast and marmalade as they could eat. It made his mouth water just thinking about that crispy bacon, those juicy mushrooms.

He wondered whether he would find that Nellie had aged when he got home, and what about Johnnie? He had been so ill and now he had become a father. He longed to see them all again and felt impatient at the Allies' slow progress.

"I don't understand why they can't just crack on with it," he said.

"It takes time, I suppose," said Rob. "Hitler's not ready to eat humble pie yet and, until he does, the war goes on."

In September Jimmy told of Operation Market Garden, the Battle of Arnhem. It was bad news for the Allies as they were halted in the Netherlands and would have to dig in for the winter. Brian's hopes of a speedy release dwindled.

"I'm going to have to start knitting. How many stitches will I need for a sweater?" he asked John who had become a knitting expert. He sized Brian up, looked at his home-made needles and his four strands of wool.

"What's the deal?"

Advice didn't come free and Brian offered a couple of cigarettes.

"About 80 stitches should do the back. Get them cast on and then you need to do three inches of ribbing." John gave the instructions and Brian got started.

"In, round, through and off," he muttered under his breath. "Plain, purl, plain, purl." He kept at it, knitting in every spare moment and he had plenty of those. Brian made slow progress but it helped to pass the time, those vast swathes of time in the rooms as the evenings drew in and the leaves on the lime trees turned golden, then brown before they fell to the ground.

"Look at this, Rob." Brian's fingers caressed Margery's letter. "It's just arrived but Margery wrote it in May; that's five months ago. I haven't the foggiest why the post's taking so long."

"It's the same for me, old boy. I've only had four letters in the last six months. I wish they'd buck up."

Elliot said that the Red Cross found it tricky getting the post through the fighting as their lines of communication had been disrupted.

"I wish they'd buck up. Margery and I need to talk about our plans."

The airmail forms were so small, little more than a postage stamp, and there was a lot to settle, their wedding, their home, their children. He knew Margery was keen to start a family and she had waited so long and so faithfully but he couldn't help thinking about the snags. Even when the war ended, he'd still be in the Army, and then when he was demobbed they'd need somewhere to live. He doubted the wisdom of cracking on with babies until they had a home, a place suitable for Margery to look after children. He chose his words to convey his concerns and his love, his enduring love. He wished the Germans would surrender, then they'd all go home before you had time to say 'Jack Robinson'. If they gave in tomorrow, he might arrive home before this letter. That would be grand, every *Kriegies'* dream; but, just in case, he'd better keep on knitting.

Eichstätt, Winter 1945

When the frost beaded the bare branches of the lime trees, the Red Cross parcels stopped coming. The *Redders* had been the *Kriegies'* lifeline; they would not have survived on Goon rations. Now they were back where they started, eating cabbage soup, black bread and potatoes; he began to feel listless as his stomach cramped with hunger.

"Elliot says we're going to be issued with the diet supplement parcels," Brian told Rob as they sat in their room spooning up their watery soup, the Goon rations.

"I thought those were for invalids," said Rob. "To give them a little bit extra."

"They are usually," said Brian. "But they're all we've got right now. It might be rather fun trying to work out our menus." Brian's trousers hung loose, flapping around his waist but at least he had finished his sweater and he needed the extra layer against the bitter cold as fuel ran short. Germany was in a stranglehold and the *Kriegies* were suffering as well as the Goons. Everyone began to look hollow-eyed.

Then Blätters shot his final bolt. As if to remind the *Kriegies* of his authority, he announced at *Appell* that all mattresses, stools and chairs would be removed from the *Kriegies*, as a reprisal for alleged mistreatment of German prisoners.

"That really takes the biscuit." Brian shivered in his greatcoat as he wrapped himself in his blankets and lay down on his bare bed boards. The Bavarian winter was bitter cold and Brian wore his new sweater day and night. His stomach grumbled, the cold air crept in like icy fingers gripping his toes, his ears, his nose and keeping him awake; he felt light-headed. Would he ever get back to Margery?

"I can't take much more, Rob. I'm thoroughly browned off."

"Hang on, old boy, put a brave face on it. It can't be long now."

Jimmy said the war had come full circle. The Allies were back in the Ardennes fighting the Battle of the Bulge.

"Jimmy says the Huns have launched a counter-offensive to force a negotiated peace. It's holding things up," said Rob.

"Well, I wish they'd get a move on. Damn Hitler! Doesn't he know he's delaying my wedding?"

"That's the spirit." Rob was glad to see Brian's sense of humour return. Amidst these dark days came a speck of light. A Red Cross lorry, loaded with parcels, broke down outside their camp.

"Have you conked out? Can we have that lot?" The *Kriegies* shouted, peering through the wire. The driver shook his head and put his thumb down; his orders were to take his cargo to another camp but his lorry wouldn't move. Something had broken and the truck must be unloaded before it could be fixed.

"We'll help you with that," the *Kriegies* cried. The Goons let them and the parcels vanished, like a puff of smoke. The *Kriegies* used their bounty to replenish their strength and Brian's will to live returned.

Then the Battle of the Bulge was over. The *Kriegies* rejoiced as the Allies moved forward and crossed the frontier into Germany. The British Army swept north towards Hamburg, the Red Army moved in from the east while the Americans pushed south towards Eichstätt, trapping the Germans in a pincer movement. But still Hitler didn't surrender.

"I can't understand why this war goes on," said Brian. "Surely, the Huns can see that there's only one possible outcome? It's such a bloody waste." Brian thumped his fist on the table. "Haven't enough people died already?" He thought of Martin, with all his life ahead of him, Simon who never lived to see his baby, Larry who had been shot when he ran for the wire in Laufen and many, many more who went to war but would never go home. "Hitler's a madman."

Elliot caught up with Brian after *Appell.*

"The SBO's worried. We know the end is coming but we don't know quite what will happen to us."

"How do you mean?" Although Brian dreamed every day about the end of the war, he had never considered the details.

"The Geneva Convention says that POWs must be held away from the fighting and as the Allies advance the Goons are moving prisoners away from the war zone. Those in Poland, for example, are already marching west."

"That must be damned hard on them, marching and sleeping rough in these temperatures."

"Yes, it's tantamount to murder," said Elliot. Brian shuddered as Elliot's words hit home; surely he couldn't have waited all this time just to...? Elliot explained the possible scenarios: a march, a German surrender, Red Cross intervention, or worst case, shot by the SS. Brian's mind rushed back to that wall in the nuns' garden; he felt sick and his mouth went dry.

"You mean... like in Hazebrouck?" Brian said.

"Yes, old boy" Elliot nodded. "It would go against the Geneva Convention, but they murdered their prisoners on the Eastern Front back in 1941 and Hitler might get desperate. We just don't know what to expect."

Brian felt as unsafe as he had in Laufen back in 1940. Food and fuel were in short supply and the *Kriegies* became skeleton thin. Brian's ribs stuck out and he dreamed of food, by day and by night. The Goons organised work parties and *Kriegies* went out daily to gather sticks and pinecones for the stoves. Brian's mood lifted with these days in the forest, returning as darkness fell.

"It's just grand to be outside the wire, to smell the pine needles and to hear the wind in the fir trees. There are green leaves on the honeysuckle and the countryside is beginning to wake up. It makes me feel there's hope in the world."

"We must hang on; it can't be long now," said Rob.

They knew the end was near; it had to be. In April, Jimmy said the US forces had crossed the Rhine and moved further south. One day, Brian and Rob heard engines, looked up and saw US planes overhead.

"I hope they know we're here," said Rob.

"Elliot says they've got all the camps marked out, to avoid mistakes," Brian said. By the middle of April, Brian heard guns rumbling in the distance; he felt the earth quiver and knew the fighting was close.

"The Yanks are coming at last," Brian said.

Elliot said that Blätters wanted to move the *Kriegies* but the SBO was reluctant. One morning at *Appell*, the Goons looked agitated as Blätters told the *Kriegies* to be ready to leave the camp in two days' time.

"The Goons are taking us to Moosberg," said Elliot. "We've protested but it's not much good. Be on your guard, Brian. Anything might happen."

Brian's mouth went dry, his stomach clenched and his mind spun; he must watch out for himself.

On the morning of 14th April, Brian, Rob and Bob lined up on the parade ground with their kitbags. Block by block the prisoners formed a column and marched out of the camp, three thousand men on the move together.

"Left... left... left, right, left."

They marched along *Adolf Hitler Strasse*, six thousand boots stamping the ground as the men snaked along the valley. On one side the ground rose steeply, dense with pines and fir trees, the camp was below them on the right and ahead the valley opened out into broad farmland. They went south in a long column of marching men.

Weak though he was, Brian stepped out smartly, wearing his sweater and his greatcoat; in his kitbag, he had food, a blanket and a change of clothes. He and Rob marched side by side. They had passed through the camp gates to reach the road when they heard engines throbbing overhead. The Goons poked them with their rifles and, without breaking step, they looked up. It was eight American Thunderbolt jets.

"The Yanks, the Yanks. Hurrah!"

The cry echoed along the column. The planes circled and flew low over the marching men and then they banked, turned and returned, diving low towards the officers and opening fire on those at the head of the column.

"Quick, take cover," yelled Elliot.

Brian dropped to the ground, scraping his hands and knees on the gritty road, and put his hands over his head. He heard the roar of the engines, the whistle of bullets and saw the spray of dirt as they hit the ground. Men screamed and yelled, clutching their arms, their heads, their legs. He saw Alan go down in a hail of bullets, blood seeping through his greatcoat. Jack and Tom lay in the road, motionless bundles in British Army uniform.

He crawled for cover in the pine trees and saw Rob wriggling along on his stomach. Bob rolled down the bank out of the line of fire. Brian kept his hands over his head and prayed as the jets passed over and turned to swoop again. He trembled all over; his legs felt weak, his stomach clenched and tears ran down his cheeks. He was alive, Rob was alive and Bob and Elliot, but others weren't. Men with whom he had shared a room, played bridge, passed the time of day, lay dead or dying in the road – and all from friendly fire. It wasn't right; it wasn't fair. Rob and Brian lay flat in the undergrowth and watched the jets circle and dive once more, raining down bullets. Brian felt his composure, his self-control vanishing, unravelling like a bad piece of knitting.

CHAPTER 27

England, March 1945

"Bye, bye," said Margery, waving at baby Andrew as he smiled from his pram. He looked sweet wearing a white fluffy cap and a little coat; Margery loved playing with him, watching him crawl, hearing him stumble over his first words. He was going to the shops with Paddy while Fleda and Margery turned the other way and headed for the common. Margery noticed daffodils, bright yellow garlands along the verges. She'd heard that the Dutch had been eating daffodil bulbs as food was scarce in the Nazi occupied territories. There was a fresh wind blowing off the common and Margery and Fleda wore scarves and gloves.

"I miss Judy so much, Fleda. She was my faithful companion and I told her all my secrets."

"Yes, you must be grieving but you did the right thing. You didn't let her suffer."

"I know it was best for her but…" Margery had known she must let her go. She should be used to partings; this war had brought so many. Brian had been one of the first to go and she'd been waiting for their wedding ever since. Paddy, always ready for a party, had started thinking about Margery's wedding.

"You can borrow Sheila's dress, Curly. You're about the same size." Paddy was a good organiser and wanted to help but Margery was superstitious; she kept her fingers crossed but she hadn't heard from Brian since Christmas. He would come back; she wouldn't let doubt creep in.

"Tell me about this cottage we're going to see," said Fleda.

"It's called Folly Lodge and Mum heard about it the other day in the butcher's shop. An old couple used to live there but they both died a couple of years ago and it's been empty ever since."

"Sounds promising then."

"We'll see. The only other place I've found is a flat in Chobham above the bank. Brian and I could have that but I'm not sure. It's got no garden, not even a backyard, and it's bound to be noisy on the High Street."

Margery and Brian had dreamed of a little cottage in the country and they couldn't have pets in a flat; she ached for another dog.

"I thought I'd heard that you and Brian were going to live at Stone Cottage?"

"To tell the truth, I'd rather we started out on our own. Brian and I have got a lot of catching up to do and we need a place to ourselves. I want to have somewhere lined up for the two of us, all ready for when he gets back."

"The war must be over soon; everyone says so. And then Brian will be back and Bob's your uncle." Fleda was always positive; she bucked Margery's spirits up.

"I hope so. I'm keeping my fingers crossed but..."

"Of course, he's all right." Fleda wouldn't admit any other option. She and Margery turned right off the road and picked their way between the puddles along a wide gravel track; it was bounded by heather and the gorse was in flower, a splash of springtime yellow. After half a mile they came to a little cottage set on its own in a large plot of ground. Margery noticed squirrels running up and down the pine trees and a blackbird greeted them from the branch of a silver birch tree. The buds on the hawthorn were spreading a vibrant green cloak over the hedgerow with primroses snuggling at the base and Margery's heart lifted. This would be a good place to start married life.

"More field than garden, I'd say," said Fleda.

"We can sort that, I'm sure. Let's go inside."

The cottage wasn't locked; it was small and dark, just two rooms and a kitchen. Margery noticed that leaves had drifted under the door and dusty cobwebs draped the windows. It was neglected and dirty but her heart lifted; she felt as if the cottage had been waiting for her.

"Where's the lav?" said Fleda.

"It's outside. That's a snag, of course."

Brian would enjoy the garden; he'd been growing vegetables in the camps. Folly Lodge was a comfortable distance from Stone Cottage, near enough for her to walk over when she wanted company but far enough for privacy.

"This will do," she said. "Now all I need is Brian."

England, May 1945

The side window let in the morning light, shining on the wardrobe door. His letters were in there, five years of letters, stored in an old shoe box. But there hadn't been one recently. She didn't know what that meant so she just kept her fingers crossed, kept hoping.

The sound of her nephew's morning routine drifted through the thin wall, calling her from her dreams. He gurgled as his nappy was changed, protested when his face was wiped, and then she heard Paddy's voice, coaxing him into his romper suit: "One leg, two legs! There, that's a good boy."

They'd soon be finished and then she could go into the bathroom. Margery looked at the picture above her bed, *The Light of the World*, a present from her godmother, years ago. She had never liked that picture; she'd take it down, she decided. Next door was quiet now and she was on duty at 10; no time for lazing about.

I'd better take a cardigan, she thought; it's chilly for May. She arrived at her ward, men's surgical, a busy, noisy ward with metal beds crammed close together and the trolleys clattering on the bare floors. Fanny Dickens was in charge, a stickler for punctuality and routine.

"Nurse Street, Nurse Thompson, I want you to make the patients tidy. We're expecting Matron later. Off you go!"

Margery went from bed to bed, straightening sheets, adjusting bandages; Fanny Dickens wanted everything ship-shape. I think they could all die in agony but she'd be happy as long as they died tidy, Margery thought. She chatted to the patients as she worked her way along the ward.

"I'll help you change your pyjamas, Private Burton, ready for Matron."

Margery fetched the screens and took a clean pair of pyjamas from the locker. She adjusted the sheets, plumped up the pillows and moved on.

"Good morning, Corporal Burns."

"And how's your mum doing, Nurse?"

"She's well but fed up with queuing for everything."

"Aren't we all? Tell her to hang on a bit longer."

As Margery moved to the next bed, she looked at her watch; it was nearly time for lunch. The telephone rang, shrill and insistent in the echoing space. Sister went to her desk and picked up the receiver. She listened, looked at Margery, and spoke a few words. Then she called Margery to her desk. Oh dear! What have I done now? she thought.

"That was your mother, Nurse Street. You may go home now."

Margery's heart thumped and her head began to spin; she must have done something dreadful.

"Go? In the middle of my shift?"

"Yes, Nurse Street. Your young man has come home."

Margery's head was buzzing; she couldn't take in what Fanny Dickens was saying. Surely, she hadn't said what she thought she'd said? But the patient in a nearby bed had no doubts. He cried out: "Hey boys, Nurse Street's young man has come home!"

The news travelled from bed to bed while Margery remained rooted to the spot. Could it really be true?

"Go!" said Sister, giving her a little push. "And good luck!"

"Three cheers for Nurse Street. Hip, hip, hurray!" The patients cheered and the ward echoed with their noise as Margery, with tears streaming down her face, left the ward, the work and the war.

Brian stood with his hand on the gate and watched the taxi pull away. The lilac was in bloom, its sweet fragrance cloying on the morning air. A blackbird sang, echoing Brian's feelings. There had been no time to ring; he had looked at the queue for the phone box and, clutching his travel warrant, he had decided to run for the train instead. He walked up the path and, taking his cap off, he turned the door handle. His mother was at the kitchen table rolling pastry, her back to him. He thought she looked crumpled like a ball of paper, smaller than he remembered. She turned and looked as if she had seen a ghost as her hand came up to her mouth.

"It's me, Mum. I'm home – at last." He took her in his arms and gave her a kiss, feeling her bones through her dress; she was so thin.

"Brian, is it really you? I can't believe you're home. My boy, oh my boy." Tears ran down her cheeks, resting in furrows that hadn't been there five years before.

"Sit down, Mum. I'm so pleased to see you." Amy's floury hands left white stripes on her face as she wiped away the tears. Brian held her hands, the skin papery and the bones brittle as she clung to him. There was so much to say but, for now, it was enough to be there.

"I thought I heard voices..." said Frank as he came through the door. "Oh Brian! How good to see you." Frank squeezed his arm and shook his hand. "How did you get here? Why didn't you ring?"

"It's a long story, Dad. Let's sit ourselves down and have a cup of tea and I can tell you all about it. Is anyone else at home?"

"Brenda's upstairs. She's putting little Rosemary down for her nap. I'll pop round and fetch Doris, Hether and John then we can all hear your story together."

Brian helped Amy to make a pot of tea and they went through to the drawing room. He told them how the end had come.

"We woke up one morning and the Germans had gone; no-one at the gates, no-one in the sentry boxes, no-one to call us to *Appell*, that's roll call. It felt strange, eerie almost. One day they were everywhere and then... they had all gone. We just couldn't believe it."

"Where were they Uncle Brian? Had you killed them all?" said John.

"No." Brian smiled at his bloodthirsty nephew. "They stayed in their barracks, waiting for the Americans; they came later and opened the gates to the camp. We were free to walk in and out as we wanted, liberated at last. Then they set up a little snack wagon by the gates and gave us all a cup of coffee and a doughnut. Not a jam doughnut like you get from the baker's van, a real American doughnut, with a hole in the middle. We had one each, a whole doughnut for each man. That was a real treat."

He told them how the prisoners had been left to make their own way to the US Airforce base, a difficult begging journey as the officers, weak and weary, made their way across the war-ravaged countryside. But they were free and that kept them going.

"Then the Yanks put us in a plane, each man sitting in a circle drawn on the floor of the plane with a bit of chalk. They gave each of us a cutlery set, a paper bag in case we were sick and a roll of lavatory paper. When we got back to Britain we were so pleased that we threw the lavatory paper out of the back of the trucks like streamers, and do you know what? People came out of their houses and ran along behind the trucks welcoming us home like heroes."

"I'll bet they did," said Brenda. "We haven't seen lavatory paper for years; we've been using cut up newspaper." Brian clapped his hands on his knees and laughed.

"Really? I never knew that."

"There's been a lot of changes, my boy, such a lot of changes," said Frank. "But enough of that for now. What would you like to do first?"

"Well, I'd really like to go over and see Margery, if that's possible. There's so much we need to talk about." Brian noticed Frank glance at Amy.

"Mmm, I'll have to see if I can get a bit of petrol," said Hether. "Harry can probably spare me a gallon." He went off with a can in his hand to try his luck on the black market.

"All set, Brian," said Hether. "Have you rung Stone Cottage?"

"Yes, they're expecting us. I've spoken to Mrs Street. Margery's on duty but she's going to ring the hospital." Brian had written to Margery, he had dreamed of her, he had planned his future with her but he hadn't seen her for over five years. His throat clenched and his stomach churned. She would be as beautiful as ever; he was sure of that. But what would she think of him? She would still be his angel, his sweetheart; but would she still love him, want to marry him? This was such a tremendous moment; he felt he was standing on the edge of a precipice.

"Please can I come too, Father?" said John.

"All right." John climbed into the back seat. Brian turned round to talk to his nephew. The difference between the toddler he'd left behind and the eleven year old schoolboy chatting about 'British Bulldog', the game he played at school, emphasised the time he had been away. As they drove down the hill into West End Brian noticed a young woman walking towards them.

"It's Margery!" he shouted. He swung open the car door and leapt out while the vehicle was still moving. He rushed across the road and swept her into his arms, squeezing her and kissing her as she pulled him towards the common. They held hands as they ran along the track until the silver birch trees hid them from view.

23rd May 1945

Brian and Margery were married in West End church on his first leave.

England, February 2017

We gathered in the church for the service, the old Norman church where our family weddings, christenings and funerals had been held for the past seventy years. We're quite a clan I thought as I looked at my grandchildren, tidy, brushed and clean for the occasion. I wondered what they would remember about my parents, their great grandparents, people who had lived, loved, laughed and cried long before they were born. The four year old, his fair curls framing his still baby face, wouldn't remember much. He passed the service, below the dusty wooden pew, running his red car along the tapestry kneeler. His older cousins listened to the eulogy; they should have stronger memories.

"I never knew Great Granny could ride a horse. How did she do that when she couldn't use her legs?" My granddaughter only remembered my mother's final years, a

wizened, bent, old woman spending her days dozing in a recliner chair. I remembered my child's eye view of my father as a bowler-hatted banker, cautious and correct, who left the house every morning to catch the 7.15 train to Waterloo. I never knew him as a passionate lover or as a soldier eager to go to France with the British Army. People are like a kaleidoscope; we see just one of the patterns.

"I knew Great Grandad went to the war and was captured by the Germans, but I thought he died in prison camp and never came back," said Daniel, my grandson.

Children don't have a clear timeline; my siblings and I were all post-war babies, the future my parents never thought they'd have. Daniel didn't know that; he had listened to adult conversation, had picked up half-heard remarks about his great granddad who had died before he was born and had tried to piece it all together.

I had done just that with my parents' story of the Second World War. I had laughed at the family joke about their wedding-that-didn't happen and had accepted it: I had never connected their lives with Dunkirk. For my grandchildren, my parents' wartime lives were remote; they were history, were school topic work like 'The Tudors' and 'The Victorians'.

When I had entered the church, I had noticed my cousins, Johnnie's daughters, sitting in a pew near the door.

"It's good of you to come," I greeted them.

"Auntie Curly was the last survivor of that generation," they said. She had outlived them all; Brian, Johnnie, Paddy and Nellie were long gone and those wartime days in Stone Cottage lingered only as shadows from our childhood.

Tim, my brother, stood to give his reading, a family poem he called it, the one that Johnnie had written for my mother, Evelyn Margery, on her wedding day, 23rd May 1945.

This is the tale of Evelyn Marge
Whose feet were extra special large
And when she walked the town about
The little boys would clown and shout
"She hasn't got a pair of feet
It's all that's left of Hitler's fleet!"

It was a period piece written in jest by her brother as Second World War, that momentous episode in Europe's history, came to an end.

Now on her happy wedding morn
She trimmed her only painful corn
And with a most tremendous squeeze
She donned a pair of narrow threes.

Mum's feet had been unusually large; she had difficulty buying shoes.

Then as she tripped along the aisle
She wore the most engaging smile
And while old Brian was sadly waiting
One foot slipped down the narrow grating.
She struggled with a mighty shout
"Please someone come and let me out!"
But everyone was left aghast
While Curlylocks was still stuck fast.

I looked at my cousins. They had always called my mother 'Auntie Curly' keeping to Johnnie's childhood nickname. She loved that reminder of their teasing brother-sister relationship.

> She gave a most tremendous lurch
> Which seemed to rock the West End church.
> This struggle was to no avail
> For t'other foot caught in the rail.
> So there she was in painful posture
> And poor old Bri said:
> "Streuth! I've lost her."
> But Curly never was a one
> So easily to overcome
> For like an agile little nipper
> She jumped out of each fastened slipper.
> Then in her darned silk stockinged feet
> She quickly lost the name of Street!

The rhyming couplets of Johnnie's verses had teased their way into family legend; they had been read at family Christmases, at birthdays and at my parents' Golden Wedding Service in May 1995. As the words rang out in the village church, the congregation rocked with laughter, a fitting memorial to my parents' long and happy lives.

BRIAN ARTHUR DOWLING
1916 – 2004

EVELYN MARGERY DOWLING (née Street)
1919 – 2017

PRINTED AND BOUND BY:

Copytech (UK) Limited trading as Printondemand-worldwide,
9 Culley Court, Bakewell Road, Orton Southgate.
Peterborough, PE2 6XD, United Kingdom.